THE LAFIYA GUIDE

A Congregational Handbook

All scripture passages are from the New Revised
Standard Version unless otherwise noted.

Project Director: Jay A. Gibble
Contributing Writers: Constance C. Conrad, Thomas A.
Droege, Dena Gilbert, David Hilton
Editor: Ronda Oosterhoff
Design: Randy Maid

TABLE OF CONTENTS

FOREWORD

In this age of health promotion, health education, health prevention, and all the economic and theological concerns that challenge our resources and talents, one might question the need to consider health in a wholistic Christian context. Yet the need is there. Within Christianity, the focus on service has often led to a habit of self-sacrifice and denial. These habits in moderation are healthy, but in excess they can lead to questionable life-styles. Along with this tradition are the ever-increasing problems of stressful living in today's modern world.

To consider these issues in the life of the church, a ministry of whole-person health must be addressed by each Christian and our communities of faith. As always, scripture is useful to this search. Reflect on a common concern of Americans—weight control—by reading Isaiah 58:3-5 below. This passage of scripture tells us how Christians might see the health habit of fasting in a unique perspective.

> " 'Why do we fast, but you do not see? Why humble ourselves, but you do not notice?' Look, you serve your own interest on your fast day, and oppress all your workers.
> Look, you fast only to quarrel and to fight and to strike with a wicked fist. Such fasting as you do today will not make your voice heard on high.
> Is such the fast that I choose, a day to humble oneself? Is it to bow down the head like a bulrush, and to lie in sackcloth and ashes? Will you call this a fast, a day acceptable to the Lord?"

It is clear that the biblical writer challenges the fast to focus on a search for the holy. It is not a fast to develop bodies fit for fighting, or to achieve holier-than-thou approaches to wellness. It is not the punishment of self-sacrifice. So what is it? Is this what secular health movements are all about? Below, Isaiah 58:6-9 presents a broader base for a whole-person health ministry.

> " Is not this the fast that I choose: to loose the bonds of injustice, to undo the thongs of the yoke, to let the oppressed go free, and to break every yoke?
> Is it not to share your bread with the hungry, and bring the homeless poor into your house; when you see the naked, to cover them, and not to hide yourself from your own kin?
> Then your light shall break forth like the dawn, and your healing shall spring up quickly; your vindicator shall go before you, the glory of the Lord shall be your rear guard.
> Then you shall call, and the Lord will answer; you shall cry for help, and he will say, Here I am."

For the Christian, the search for health and healing is centered in mind-body-spirit wholeness for self and community. The Bible clearly indicates that this is true. The path for the Christian is LAFIYA. It is more than self; it is more than disease. It is more than a program or self-help group. It is a continuing journey of self and the community of faith toward health and wholeness.

For this reason, *The Lafiya Guide* is a welcome resource from the Association of Brethren Caregivers (ABC) to the wider church. The use of the *Guide* in the community of faith will help our light to "break forth," our healing to "quickly appear," and our Lord to say, "Here I am." Use the *Guide* in your journey, and I hope our paths will meet in this mutual search.

Lafiya,

Dr. Tana Durnbaugh, RN
President
Association of
Brethren Caregivers,
Elgin, Illinois

ACKNOWLEDGEMENTS

Many people have contributed to the development of *The Lafiya Guide* and to the vision of a congregational-based, whole-person health ministry. Special recognition must go to the Nigerian Church, Ekklesiyar Yanuwa a Nigeria, for both the name and the concept. Mission planners and Nigerian health workers established a community-based health approach in the 1970s under the name *Lafiya*. The focus was to train village health workers in primary health care and disease prevention. That approach—shifting from expensive medical treatment to education and prevention—changed the health care system in many Nigerian villages.

Through their experience in Nigeria, several missionary doctors became enthusiastic about the effectiveness of health care that stemmed from a preventative and educational perspective. They returned to the United States with stories that challenged churches to become involved with health, healing, and wholeness ministries as an integral part of faith. Key voices in this effort have been Drs. James Kipp, Norman Waggy, and David Hilton.

James Kipp inspired audiences with his speech "The Church as a Healing Community." Norman Waggy was a member of a special consultation to shape the program "Lafiya: A Whole-person Health Ministry" and advocated the use the the Lafiya name. David Hilton served as an ongoing consultant in the development of the Lafiya program for congregations in the United States.

As this *Guide* goes to press, the Lafiya whole-person health ministry has been launched in ten Church of the Brethren congregations. Though they are at various phases of implementing Lafiya ministry principles into congregational life, they all share the Lafiya vision of health and healing—a whole-person ministry that includes body, mind, and spirit. Many of their experiences are reflected in this handbook. These ten pilot congregations are in Crest Manor, Indiana; Daleville, Virginia; Elizabethtown, Pennsylvania; Germantown, Pennsylvania; Lansing, Michigan; Manchester, Indiana; McPherson, Kansas; Columbus, Ohio; Plymouth, Indiana; and Roanoke, Virginia.

Beyond these ten pilot congregations, many others helped shape the vision for Lafiya. Denominational wholistic health task forces under the leadership of Steve Tuttle, Carolyn Weddle, and Julie Liggett initially provided the energy that prodded the development of Lafiya. Other task groups called for congregations to become safe places for health and healing. Recent presidents of the Brethren Health and Welfare Association (BHWA), now the Association of Brethren Caregivers (ABC)—James Kipp, Mary Sue Resenberger, Mary Ann Harvey, Warren Eshbach, and Tana Durnbaugh—have all challenged ABC to engage congregations in health and healing ministries. Ron Finney, associate district executive for northern Indiana, has helped field-test some Lafiya resources. Ann Raber, on staff with the Mennonite Mutual Aid Association's Wellness Program, has led a series of district workshops on congregational wellness. In the formation of Lafiya, Granger Westberg gave a motivational speech for congregations to move into health and healing ministries. Donald Miller, general secretary to the General Board of the Church of the Brethren, was most helpful in advocating Lafiya's inclusion in the Brethren's allocation of funds for the 1990s. Without that funding source, Lafiya could not have been developed. These and many others have helped shape the development of Lafiya.

Five primary writers contributed to this project. David Hilton, presently a denominational and congregational health consultant and formerly with the Christian Medical Commission of the World Council of Churches, provided the introduction and background materials. Thomas Droege, health consultant with the Carter Center and former theology professor, provided the theological section and served as writing coordinator. Jay Gibble, executive director of ABC and current staff for Lafiya, developed the Lafiya program sections. Constance Conrad, health consultant and retired Emory University faculty member from Atlanta, Georgia, provided the resource pages, and Dena Gilbert, Bethany Theological Seminary student intern, developed the suggested helps for the Lafiya care group section.

INTRODUCTION

Surveys consistently report that one of people's most important concerns is their health. We all want to be healthy. Yet seldom do we seriously consider the question "What is health?" Below is a look at how the Lafiya concept of health came into being.

Lafiya: a gift from Nigeria to the USA

In the 1970s, Church of the Brethren Mission (CBM) workers learned about health in a new way as they served Lardin Gabas, a 10,000 square mile area in northeastern Nigeria. The missionaries noted that almost half of the children were dying before age five, mostly from preventable diseases. Missionaries treated thousands of people, but it became increasingly apparent that most of the patients returned home only to contract the same illnesses again.

In 1974, a committee of missionaries and Nigerians decided to emphasize community involvement in preventative medicine. The result was the Lafiya program. "Lafiya" is a word in the Hausa language that means "well being," or "wholeness." It can also mean "How are you?" ("Lafiya?") as well as "I am well" ("Lafiya!"). The customary greeting exchange goes on for a long time, with people asking "Is your wife lafiya? Are your children lafiya? Your farm? Work?" And so on.

The strength of the Lafiya program in Nigeria is its well-trained, community-based village health workers. A community organizer helps form a village health committee representing all segments of the community. The committee chooses a man and a woman from the community to be health promoters. The health promoters are trained to communicate health awareness and preventative strategies through local folk media such as stories and songs. Since the health workers are well known to, and chosen by, the villagers, their activities become not only accepted but expected by the community.

The results of the Nigerian Lafiya program have been impressive. In 1989 there were 67 active Village Health Posts in the Lardin Gabas area. In most of these villages, health has improved dramatically. For example, mothers learned how to prevent deaths from dehydration by giving a mixture of salt, sugar, and water to their children. Deaths from malaria, caused by a mosquito-borne blood parasite, were prevented by eliminating mosquito breeding places and giving children under five—the most vulnerable—a small dose of preventive medicine each month. Some communities have reported that, "No child has died in our village since the health promoters started work!" The people of Lardin Gabas have demonstrated that, when given the right information and motivation, people can make a great impact on their own health.

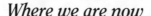

Where we are now

In the United States, we have a condition similar to what existed in Lardin Gabas prior to Lafiya. Here, too, we often try to bring health simply by curing disease. We do not have a health care system, but rather a "disease cure" system. Many times we focus on sickness and restoring health rather than on preventing and promoting good health. It is wonderful, and essential, to have skilled medical professionals to treat us when we get sick. But when this is the major focus of the system, a crisis develops.

Some may not agree that a health crisis has indeed developed in a privileged nation like the United States. However, Russell Morgan of the National Council for International Health reports that:

• While life expectancy in Singapore is 74 years, for U.S. African-Americans it is 64.8.

• Eighteen out of every thousand African-American women die in childbirth in the U.S., while in Kuwait the number is six women per thousand.

• Sixteen of every thousand infants born in Jamaica in 1989 died, while in the District of Columbia the figure was over 22 per thousand.

• Thirteen and a half percent of African-American babies in the U.S. are low birth weight, while in Egypt the figure is only five percent.

• Ten percent of all babies born in the U.S. have been exposed to alcohol or other addictive substances.

• The measles rate in Costa Rica is less than half a percent, while in Los Angeles it is 15 percent, a 500 percent jump from the previous year's statistic.

• The U.S.'s 82 percent immunization rate places it 56th in the world.

• One-fourth of sexually active teens in the U.S. will contract a sexually transmitted disease by age 21.

• In the U.S. AIDS is increasing by 30 percent a year. Seventy percent of diagnosed cases have died.

Additionally,

• Limited housing for the poor leads to unsanitary conditions and homelessness, which threatens health.

• Many city dwellers spend one-third of the year breathing air with pollution levels well above government standards.

• More than 30 million Americans have no access to health care, and thousands lose their health insurance as they become unemployed or develop serious illness.

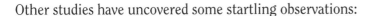

Other studies have uncovered some startling observations:

• The Carter Center of Emory University has concluded after an extensive study that the leading causes of death in the United States are tobacco, alcohol, and violence. For young people living in cities the most common cause of death is homicide.

• Most illnesses are caused by what we do to ourselves, both individually and collectively. A report of a worldwide study by the Christian Medical Commission in Geneva reminds us that health is not primarily medical, but rather an integral part of justice, peace, environment, and personal life-style. The highest cause of illness in the world is poverty. These problems are beyond the competence of medicine and are best dealt with by changing behaviors and socioeconomic conditions.

• The surgeon general has been reporting for years that over 80 percent of all illnesses in the United States are preventable. Therefore we must complete our disease cure system by making it a health care system that focuses on keeping people well. The Lafiya experience in Nigeria has shown that this can be done by empowering people to take health into their own hands.

Progress, but not enough

Ironically, the preventative approach has been lost in the West, perhaps mostly due to the rapid advance of modern medicine. We have been slow to respond to the need for health promotion, so deep are our predispositions to cure rather than to prevent disease.

But we are now reaching a point where the "curable" diseases, such as polio, have met their match in penicillin and a host of versatile antibiotics. The diseases that are left—cancer, AIDS, heart disease, cirrhosis of the liver, and others—did not establish themselves in a human body overnight, nor can they be eradicated that easily. Most doctors now agree that the best antidotes for modern diseases are long-term, preventative, healthy life-style choices.

Still, many of us choose to wait and hope these afflictions do not happen to us. We fail to understand that we could save ourselves physical pain, worry, and unnecessary expense by adopting a proactive, rather than reactive approach to personal health.

But finally, more of us, Christians included, are taking a greater responsibility for personal health. We can watch and learn from the discoveries of modern medicine—much of which will confirm what we already suspect: psychologists, sociologists, and doctors are starting to agree that behavior, attitude, spirituality, and physical health are intricately related. Recent studies show that, in addition to the outbreak of the human immuno virus HIV, which leaves the body unable to fight off normal diseases, some of the strongest immune system suppressors are feelings such as unresolved guilt,

anger, resentment, and meaninglessness. And some of the strongest immunity builders are loving relationships in community. Should we as Christians be surprised?

These findings have enormous implications for the church and for each of us as Christians. The gospel of Jesus Christ addresses each factor—all related to sin, of course—that plays a part in suppressing the immune system. So it turns out that the real places of health for Christians should not be hospitals but rather the warmth and acceptance we find in our Christian communities.

Lafiya's challenge to the churches in the USA

We have seen that there is an urgent need to complete the health care system in our country by empowering people to take health back into their own hands. To be empowered, people need a rallying point. What better organization to serve this function than the church?

Churches are among the few remaining examples of community in this country. Churches provide a rallying point around which persons may share their faith, their concerns, their worship of God, and their lives. Here issues of justice, peace, environment, and life-style can be addressed within the framework of the gospel, Christian tradition, and the indwelling of the Holy Spirit.

With a supportive Christian community we can more easily make decisions about our lives that help us and others find real "life"—physical, mental, and spiritual. Health education is most effective when, with others, we are seeking answers to health questions. When we support each other in bad times and good, health is promoted. When we create a safe place to tell each other our stories of pain and brokenness we can become healing communities.

Doctors who take time to listen to their patients often hear them say, "I have never told anyone this in my life," and then pour out a story of agony and suffering. Very often simply telling the story to a sympathetic and non-judgmental listener results in relief of illness, both emotional and physical. It does not take years of professional training to be this kind of listener. We can all learn to create a place where it is safe to share our life stories with each other and become healing communities. What is required is that we respect—love—one another enough to listen, carefully and without judging.

The question is: How do we translate this knowledge into action that leads to health? The Lafiya program suggests activities that will help us on the journey toward being communities of healing and wholeness. What follows are guidelines; groups will need to find what works best for their members, each of whom has unique gifts and problems that they can learn to share with others on the same journey. Together we will grow toward the potential that God has given each of us: abundant life.

PART 1

Lafiya Foundations

Laying Faith Foundations for a Lafiya Ministry

LAFIYA FOUNDATIONS

Laying Faith Foundations for a Lafiya Ministry

Lafiya is a new way of doing ministry. Though some of us may be cautious about embracing the idea of "wholeness"—spiritual, relational, and physical well-being—we can trace the idea all the way back to the healing ministry of Jesus. In this section of *The Lafiya Guide* we want to concentrate on exploring the faith foundations of Lafiya's ministry of health and healing.

It is essential that we have a solid biblical and theological foundation for anything we do in the church, but that's particularly true when we are concerned with spiritual matters that relate to salvation, which ultimately means "wholeness." The particular concern of Lafiya is to help people assume responsibility for their own health within the company of others who care for each other through listening, empowering, and resourcing. What is the biblical mandate for such a ministry and what are its theological underpinnings?

The church's healing ministry

Even a cursory reading of the gospels shows how central healing was in the ministry of Jesus. Healing means restoration to wholeness, the wholeness God intends for body, mind, and spirit. That's certainly what Jesus' ministry was all about. One-third of the stories in the gospels are stories of Jesus physically healing people. If we broaden the definition of "healing" to include spiritual and relational healing, then all stories about Jesus address some form of healing. Jesus came to "save," and the meaning of that word in its original Greek is "to heal." In fact, biblical Greek has only one word for those two terms, a word that is sometimes translated "save" and sometimes "heal," depending on the context.

A good example of Jesus' whole-person healing ministry is the story of the

A Biblical Vision for Lafiya

"The Spirit of the Lord God has anointed me (is) . . .

. . . to bring good news to the oppressed,
. . . to bind up the brokenhearted,
. . . to proclaim liberty to the captives,
. . . to opening the prison to those who are bound,
. . . and to comfort all who mourn.

I was burdened with guilt,
    And you listened without blame;
I was imprisoned in addictive behaviors,
    And you empowered me to make
    healthy choices;
I was intimidated by abusive relationships,
    And you surrounded me with
    caring friends;
I was overcome by fear and despair,
    And you came to me with healing
    resources;
I was consumed by anger and alienation,
    And you met me with forgiving love.

"Just as you have ministered to one of the least of these who are members of my family, you did it to me."

       Paraphrase of Isaiah 61:1-2;
       Matthew 25:35-36, 40

paralytic who is brought to Jesus by four friends (Mark 2:1-12). It's obvious the friends wanted Jesus to heal the paralyzed man; they were so determined to gain access to him that they broke a hole in the roof of the house where Jesus was speaking to a crowd of people. But instead of healing him, Jesus forgave him. Some religious leaders in the crowd disputed his authority to forgive sins, so Jesus settled the dispute by saying to the paralytic, "Stand up, take your mat and go to your home" (Mark 2:11).

Where one may expect Jesus to heal, he forgives, and where he forgives, he also heals. That's characteristic of whole-person healing ministry, and the gospels are full of stories like that. If healing was so central to Jesus' ministry, then isn't this what Christians are called to do as well?

The answer of the church through the ages has been yes. We see it in the Acts of the Apostles and in the writings of the church fathers. We see it in the building of hospitals and in the sending of medical missionaries. We see it in the Pentecostal movement and in Christian Science, two prominent historic expressions of the healing mission of the church. The mandate to heal as well as to preach the gospel is a mission for every age. We must continually look for ways to bring about healing in others—those who are already in the church as well as those who have yet to accept the love and forgiveness of Jesus Christ.

The church's health ministry

The challenge for the church today is to provide *health* ministries as well as *healing* ministries. This model of health promotion, which is at the heart of the Lafiya ministry program, stems from the Church of the Brethren's involvement with the Nigerian Rural Health Project. The leaders of the Nigerian project were pioneers in empowering people to take responsibility for their own health by improving nutrition and the water supply, thus effecting dramatic changes in both the length and quality of their lives.

The wisdom of that approach is beginning to catch on in this country as well. Though 98 percent of each dollar spent on "health care" is currently for "disease care," changes are occurring. We can see it in the new kinds of research being done—research on what makes people sick, research on how attitude and behavior affect health, and research on the effects of diet and exercise. All of these are factors over which we have some control. More people are becoming aware of the need for life-style changes for health purposes than at any other time in the history of the world.

But why should the church be active in promoting health? We find rationale in the words of Jesus: "I came that they may have life, and have it abun-

dantly" (John 10:10). That means eternal life of course, but it's obvious from the gospels that it also means the abundant life here and how. Lafiya means "I am well. I am whole." Lafiya is a tree of whole-person health, one branch of which is healing ministry and another branch of which is health promotion.

Though healing ministries have always been vitally important to the church, the unique challenge for our day is health promotion. Instead of asking only "What makes people sick and how can we provide a whole-person healing ministry to heal or save them?" we need to also ask "What keeps people well and how can we provide a whole-person health ministry that will keep them that way?" That's the wave of the future in health care, and the church is the ideal medium for empowering people to assume responsibility for their own health. With the Lafiya program, we have a magnificent opportunity to provide leadership in defining and implementing the role of the church in health promotion.

The role of hope in health promotion

Why is it that among a group of people who are exposed to the same health threats some stay well while others become ill? Current studies have begun to address this question, and the answers all point to factors that have to do with faith. This makes the issue a spiritual one, and Christians need to claim their authority to address it with the resources of the Christian faith.

In answering the question about what keeps people well, we can see that hope is a factor. Perhaps you heard the news report about the ten-year-old boy who stepped off the bus into the school yard and fell over dead. The report stated that he had led a lonely life. His mother had remarried, and she and his stepfather did not provide much attention at home. At school he did not have any friends, and those that did acknowledge him poked fun at him. The autopsy revealed no abnormalities; his heart had simply stopped beating.

Any attempt to offer an explanation for such a death is speculative, but certainly hopelessness was a contributing factor. We have evidence that animals literally give up when put into situations of helplessness and hopelessness. When dogs are given unavoidable, inescapable electric shocks, they seem to accept their situation as hopeless, even when later placed in a shock situation that includes an opportunity to escape.

The same is true of rats that are put into a situation from which they cannot flee or fight, such as a jar full of water. They quickly die from a slowing of the heart and respiration. That happens even more quickly if their whiskers, a principal source of orienting themselves to their environment, have been clipped. However, if the rats are periodically and briefly put in a jar of water and released quickly each time, they will later learn to swim in the jar for long periods of time without signs of giving up or dying.

If these observations are true of animals in hopeless situations, then it is

certainly plausible that the heart of a lonely and hopeless ten-year-old boy would simply stop beating.

Hope keeps people well and facilitates healing. Hope is spiritual energy that activates the human will. It is an expression of faith. Keeping hope alive is health ministry, and no institution in society is better equipped to promote real hope than the church. Physicians can offer the hope of recovery, but faith nurtures hope in eternal life, even in the most hopeless situations.

Think of people who live with chronic illness. It is usually those with the strongest sense of hope who are able to rise above the chaos of self-disruption that accompanies chronic or fatal illness.

Benefits of belonging

A strong sense of belonging, like hope, also helps keep people well. Studies show that those who lack strong relational bonds are more vulnerable to illness. For example, heart attack victims are 50 percent more likely to have a second attack within six months if they live alone. People who are single, separated, divorced, or widowed are two to three times more likely to die earlier than their married peers. The Hammond Report, which prompted the surgeon general's warning on packs of cigarettes, states that the effects of divorce are about the same as smoking more than 20 cigarettes a day. Whether heart disease, cancer, depression, tuberculosis, arthritis, or problems during pregnancy, the occurrence of disease is higher in those with weakened social connections, especially men.

How often have you experienced or heard a story about a dying person who suddenly rallies when distant family members arrive at the bedside? Sam received a call like that. His sister, only 55 years old, was dying of cancer. Her doctor said she was very close to death—only two or three days at the most. Sam and other members of the family went to be with her. Three weeks later he had to return to his job in Atlanta, as did others in the family. Within a day of his return his sister died. One might say that the incident was poor calculation on the doctor's part, but surely the support of a loving family was an important factor in Sam's sister's will to live.

It ought to be obvious to Christians that hope and belonging, as well as other faith-related factors such as meaning and purpose, are spiritual in nature. If these factors are important in the maintenance of both spiritual and physical health, then it ought to be equally as obvious that one of the greatest challenges facing the church is to provide a whole-person health ministry that sustains hope and strengthens relationships.

Spirituality and health

Spirituality is the turf Christians need to claim as their own—not exclu-

sively, of course, but as the experts in a faith tradition that can satisfy the spiritual hunger that comes with being human. Spirituality often gets confused with religion; when we describe a person as "spiritual," we usually mean that he or she is "religious." But treating the terms as synonymous keeps us from seeing that all people are spiritual beings whether or not they regard themselves as religious. Every person has an inborn hunger for meaning, hope, and belonging—all of which are characteristic results of being created in the image of God.

Spirituality, on the other hand, is the particular form that hunger—and the satisfaction of that hunger—takes in a person's life. Spirituality exemplifies what a person trusts and is loyal to, especially at the center of his or her life. Spirituality is what a person hopes for in life, what shapes meaning and purpose in each situation and throughout life.

To make this more concrete and personal, answer the following questions:

• When you are at the end of your rope and have exhausted your own resources for coping, what or whom do you trust and remain loyal to, no matter what?

• If you were told that you had six months to live, what would be your source of hope and to whom would you turn for help?

Answers to these questions will reveal the content of one's spirituality—the extent to which one yearns for and depends on the sustenance of God.

Ultimately our spiritual needs can only be met in relationship with God. The challenge of Lafiya is not only to focus on spiritual needs but also to draw deeply from the well of faith in meeting those needs. Unless the content of spirituality is rooted in the Bible that defines our faith, Lafiya will be no different from any of other health promotion program that talks about the importance of spiritual health.

The root of spirituality: relationship with a God who heals

What do we know about God from the Bible that affects our understanding of health promotion? If God is like Jesus, then we know that God is a loving God who wants everybody to be whole. It's almost inconceivable that Jesus would say to someone who had come to be healed, "I'm sorry, but it's not God's will that you be whole." Not God's will? Of course it is God's will! Jesus' whole ministry breathes the Spirit of a God who groans in yearning for restoration of the whole creation. Illness may serve a good purpose, but God never originally intended for people to suffer.

We also know that God has created our bodies with the capacity for self-healing. The real healer is not the physician nor the medication he or she prescribes but the healer within, the God who created our bodies. Eighty percent of all health problems people bring to their physicians are self-correct-

ing, and those medical interventions that are successful simply facilitate the body's own healing power. This wonder of creation should not only prompt deep gratitude to God but also empower us to take more responsibility for our own health.

After all, each Christian person is closest to the healer that is within him or her. Individuals know their own health needs better than anyone else. Within the limits of heredity and environmental factors beyond our control, we can count on the self-healing power God has given us—provided we do what we can to avoid harming or undermining the natural workings of our bodies, which are wondrous gifts from God.

Getting people to change

It is one thing to recognize health promotion as an imminent challenge of the church. It is something else to act on it. Motivating people to change is at the heart of any health promotion program. We need to examine this question not only in terms of what will work but also in terms of what is biblically sound.

A study by Dean Ornish, a clinical professor of medicine, demonstrated that coronary heart disease can be reversed without using cholesterol-lowering drugs or surgical interventions. Ornish used the term "transformation" to explain how life-style changes affected the experimental group. Transformation, he claimed, had to do with a spirituality that was rooted in meaning, purpose, values, and communal support.

Education, we can deduce, is not enough. The surgeon general's warning on cigarette packages, nutritional guidelines on food products, resources from The Interfaith Health Resource Center at the Carter Center in Atlanta—all the information in the world will be of no help without the motivation to change. That's why the first step must be to focus attention on individual transformation, which means a reformation in the center of the self. Christians often explain conversion as spiritual transformation, but Lafiya challenges the church to broaden the definition to include a greater respect for one's body and health as well as one's spiritual reconciliation with God.

Transformation. Isn't that what the church is all about—changing people? And not just changing their mind but also their heart, their way of understanding themselves and their relationship to God? Right behavior will flow out of a mind and heart that have experienced transformation. Nobody in the health care field is better positioned to address the issue of transformation than those of us in the church. That's our uniqueness, what distinguishes us from others who are pushing health promotion—for purely physical, or self-seeking reasons—as the most important aspect of health care for the future.

Encouragement, not guilt, motivates

Transformation. How does it happen? The Bible speaks of two fundamental ways to change people—one by means of the law and the other by means of the gospel. Both have a place in scripture and both can be effective, but Christians accept the gospel over the law because of its rootedness in Christ.

Law as a method of changing people usually includes threats and generates fear. It assumes that people will change if they are fearful enough of the consequences of their actions. One gets what he or she deserves. Rewards follow good behavior, and harm follows bad.

One reason for the success of this approach is its solid scientific evidence, particularly in the health field. Linking life-style to health in health promotion means that we are responsible for our health. This is biblical. Few would dispute that there are self-destructive consequences to smoking, the lack of exercise, a poor diet, and general disregard for maintaining one's health and fitness.

But most of us don't find this approach very appealing. We don't like guilt trips and scare tactics, especially when they are used on us. This law-oriented approach encourages self-righteousness and becomes destructive when used for self-justification and blaming the victim. Consider the story of Job and the ease with which we blame others for their own physical demise ("I thank you Lord, that I am not like that physical wreck who smokes two packs of cigarettes a day, never exercises, and pigs out on pork. I eat veggies and bran, run five miles a day, and meditate a half hour each morning and evening"). Surely as Christians we can find a more positive way to motivate people.

For a more positive approach to health promotion, we need to go back to the beginning of our relationship to God—back before humanity's fall in Eden when sin entered the world—to see what God intended for humanity. Adam and Eve were given the responsibility to care for everything God had made. The world was not theirs to do with as they pleased.

By implication, we are created in the image of God to care for the world as God cares for it. That includes our bodies. Instead of saying, "This is my body, and I have a right to do with my body what I choose," a biblically informed response would be, "God has given me this body to care for, and whatever decision I make must be made in partnership with God." There can be no question about the importance of this covenant relationship to God for health ministry.

Cautions when pursuing health ministry

The Bible is full of stories that illustrate humanity's failure to be responsible caretakers of God's good creation. The record has not improved. We live

in a world where all of us have some part in abusing God's blessings. We live in a world where greed prompts businesses and governments to destroy the environment with pollutants and as a result, contaminate food with dangerous chemicals. We live in a world where people abuse their bodies through the intake of smoke, drugs, junk food, and excessive stress. We live in a world where people abuse others through physical violence, sexual harassment, and excessive demands on their time and energy. In short, we live in a fallen world where disorder describes our individual and corporate lives, and any noble attempt at order, such as the quest for wellness, easily warps into a symptom of self-seeking, self-serving idolatry.

That last thought is a warning Christians must take seriously. It is sobering for us to consider that even health promotion, when self-grounded, can be evidence of a distorted spirituality. Compulsive health seeking, which characterizes so much of what goes on in the fitness movement today, is an attempt to make life secure, to fend off illness—even death—in a futile attempt to master the forces that threaten not only our well-being, but also life itself. That's what sin is at its very core: our effort to make life secure on our own terms, by our own efforts, and thus under our own control.

All this brings us back to a point addressed before: the need for transformation. We can no longer rely on natural impulses toward well-being. Our health ministry must be rooted in the gospel, in Christ and the restored wholeness he offers through his life, death, and resurrection.

After that, the next step is to consider the implications of the gospel for whole-person health ministry. Paul sums it up this way: "Or do you not know that your body is a temple of the Holy Spirit within you, which you have from God, and that you are not your own? For you were bought with a price; therefore glorify God in your body" (I Corinthians 6:19-20). What a wonderful metaphor!

If we really consider our bodies to be temples of God, then we will treat them as sacred places consecrated by God's presence. We keep our churches clean, well-kept, and beautiful because we regard them as holy places, but we regularly treat our bodies as possessions to do with as we please—to abuse them if it brings us pleasure, and to overuse them if it brings us success. If we believe that we are not our own, including our bodies, then we will treat ourselves differently than if we believe our bodies are material objects, somehow separate from us and ours to handle according to whim.

Turning ownership of one's body back to its proper owner gives one a sense of purpose. Not only do we respect ourselves more, but we feel cared for, as if our actions have repercussions on people other than ourselves. This experience is part of the Lafiya process. People whose lives are full of hope and meaning live longer and healthier lives. It is faith in Christ that provides ultimate hope and meaning. That faith sustains us even when we face situations that seem to be hopeless, such as death. It is not a contradiction in terms to speak of "healthy dying," and the care of the dying belongs under the health ministry of Lafiya.

Mildred was a woman whose face, conversation, behavior, and whole being reflected her faith. Her 18 months of cancer afflicted her with debilitating losses and increasing pain. But her faith modeled hope to everyone who shared with her the experience of dying. Not only did she see Jesus with an inner vision that became clearer as she approached death, but those of us gathered around her bedside were privileged to witness that vision. It was a dying full of wonder and hope, in fact, a "healthy dying."

Conclusion

Let nothing less than the transformation of faith be our goal in whole-person health ministry. Lafiya acknowledges that the transformation of people and communities into restored wholeness is a gift from Christ. We are empowered to be all that God made us to be. That is the basic health message of any gospel-oriented health ministry. Not a string of moral imperatives about what to do and what not to do—eat right, exercise, don't smoke, don't isolate yourself—but a gospel of health ministry to live out the freedom of the abundant life in Christ.

If we have been transformed by the love of God into new beings, then our behavior will take care of itself. We will want to treat our bodies as temples of the Holy Spirit. We will seek out fellowship that not only meets our social needs but also our deeper need for relationship with God. We will have hope that is stronger and deeper than positive thoughts about the future, a hope that will sustain us through debilitating illnesses and up to the very hour of death. And we will have a purpose that gives deep meaning to life, a purpose that reflects the love and service of Christ, whose mission was to restore all of humanity to the fullness of life.

Health education and effective programs in nutrition and exercise are not enough. We need to go back to the basics if we are going to have a biblically based health ministry, and nothing is more basic than spiritual transformation. Let that be our top priority—today, next week, next year, and always.

THE LAFIYA SYMBOL

This symbol was created to represent the "Whole-Person Health Ministry" concept of Lafiya. The organic form of the leaf in the Lafiya symbol expresses the concept of health, growth, and life. The variation of the shape of the leaves express these concepts, with each leaf representing mind/body/spirit. The circle enclosing the leaves represents completeness and wholeness. And through the cross, we witness the interconnectedness of faith with health, healing, and wholeness.

PART 2

Lafiya Vision

Applying the Principles of Listening, Empowering, and Resourcing

LAFIYA VISION

Applying the Principles of Listening, Empowering, and Resourcing

In a safe congregation people learn the grace of walking with others as they travel their inner, yet collective, journeys of despair and weakness without criticism or judgment. One church in Illinois has adopted four principles for sharing hurts in congregational life: tell the truth, avoid gossip, remain faithful, and address conflict. With these protective principles in place, the church walked through the valley of AIDS with one of its members. Refusing to be distracted by the difficult issues surrounding the illness, church members mediated the presence and grace of Christ throughout the ordeal. The man died with the assurance of God's grace and forgiveness. His wife experienced acceptance and worth, and the children were able to cope with the agonizing cries of despair that whelmed up from within.

Healing happens in safe places

Another example of healing community is Alcoholics Anonymous (AA). Widely recognized to be the most effective treatment for addiction, AA brings together sufferers who confess that their lives are out of control, share their stories of pain and struggle, accept and forgive, and offer control of their lives to God. Together, they heal. We might ask, "Do we have to become an alcoholic to belong to such a group?" For who of us can say that we have complete control of our lives? We all have stories of anguish to share.

Unfortunately, many of our congregations are the opposite of healing communities. They are places where we pretend that we are good. Going all dressed up to Sunday morning service we say, "Isn't it wonderful to be with all these good people?" So a person suffering with guilt, doubt, resentment, or other kind of hurt or problem dare not speak of it for fear of being rejected. Indeed many alcoholics report that when their congregation learned of their problem, they no longer felt welcome there.

Finding a community where people are accepted unconditionally is a rare occurrence. On any given Sunday approximately 20 percent of those attending worship services will experience some symptom of illness because of the stress in their lives. They bring to the community their grief over losses and their worry about the future. They are waiting to hear words of hope and direction. While a congregation may indeed hear words of hope, too often members go about church "as usual" with no awareness of the pain felt by others in the gathered community. Instead of finding hope, members stifle their pain, and therefore compound it. Pain has no voice and no listener.

Lafiya will become a reality within a congregation only when members develop an awareness of and a sensitivity to the personal needs of others—no easy task. Usually, people disclose inner worlds of anxiety, fear, guilt, and addiction only to the extent that they feel safe. Too many people experience church as a place that is *not* safe to disclose their inner feelings. Thus the task of creating a safe environment—a sanctuary of safety for disclosing, or confessing, wounds and fears—is the starting point of a successful Lafiya ministry.

Creating a safe environment: applying the principles of listening, empowering, and resourcing

The Lafiya Tree is a visual representation of what Lafiya is all about. The tree represents the health of the whole person, which is what Lafiya promotes. The roots of Lafiya are listening, empowering, and resourcing. These roots draw their nourishment from a biblical understanding of Christian community. The branches express the growth that comes from a community of health and healing.

Keeping the picture of a tree in mind will help participants see Lafiya as a life-giving network, not just another program. Busy people often say—with good reason—that too many church programs undermine rather than nurture the health of individuals and families. Lafiya is not a new program but a new way to do ministry. It's a change in perspective, a different approach to all the forms of ministry a church offers: worship, education, home care, counseling, evangelism, stewardship, and all others.

Three words capture the heart of the Lafiya experience: listening, empowering, and resourcing. The means to wholeness is a sense of safety, or complete acceptance, throughout congregational life. This will happen everywhere as the principles of listening, empowering, and resourcing take hold.

Learning to apply the principles of listening, empowering, and resourcing is absolutely essential for the Lafiya way of doing ministry. The following pages will look at each of these important components.

THE LAFIYA TREE

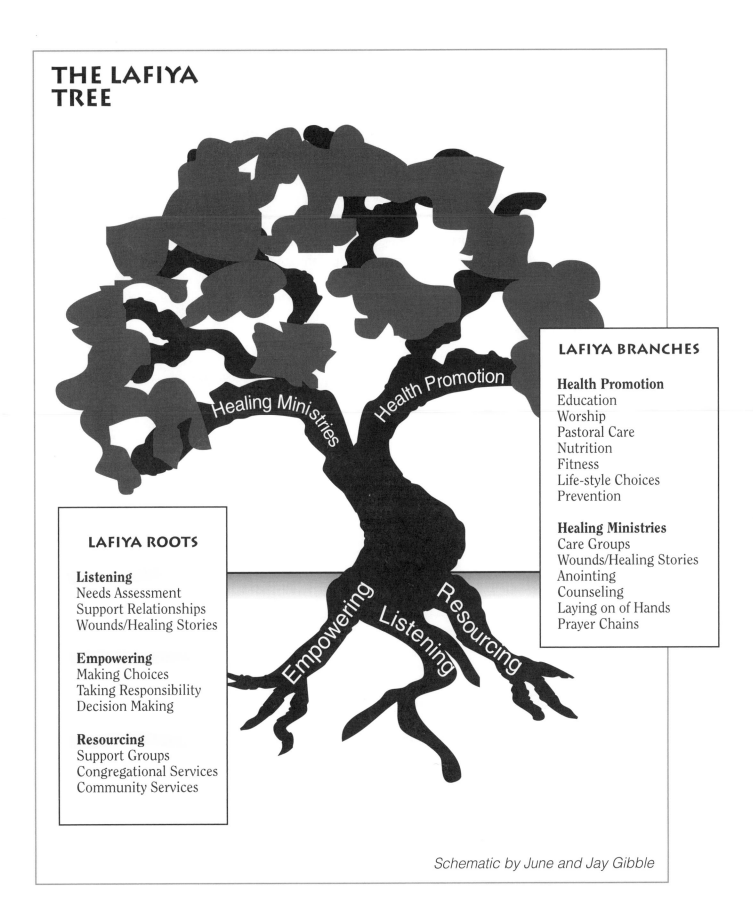

LAFIYA BRANCHES

Health Promotion
Education
Worship
Pastoral Care
Nutrition
Fitness
Life-style Choices
Prevention

Healing Ministries
Care Groups
Wounds/Healing Stories
Anointing
Counseling
Laying on of Hands
Prayer Chains

LAFIYA ROOTS

Listening
Needs Assessment
Support Relationships
Wounds/Healing Stories

Empowering
Making Choices
Taking Responsibility
Decision Making

Resourcing
Support Groups
Congregational Services
Community Services

Schematic by June and Jay Gibble

LISTENING. This is the first and most important principle because it is through listening that we empower people and help them access resources for meeting their health needs. Listening is not simply letting others talk but rather an active process that requires awareness, sensitivity, and personal engagement. Active listeners do the following:

Tune into feelings.
They allow the storyteller—the person who is sharing his or her story—to express and experience a full range of emotions. They are not embarrassed by tears.

Observe body language.
They watch the person telling the story, asking themselves, *Is this person's body language communicating the same message as what he or she is saying?* If it looks as if a storyteller is having difficulty expressing true feelings, a sensitive listener will gently share with the storyteller what he or she is observing.

Paraphrased listening.
"Reflecting," or paraphrasing, occurs when listeners repeat back to the storyteller, in a condensed, paraphrased way, how they are understanding the story. This helps clarify the meaning of the story for both the storyteller and listener.

Ask open-ended questions.
Active listeners ask questions that directly relate to the story just heard. The best questions grow out of the story itself, not the listener's agenda.

Allow time.
Active listeners also avoid rushing in to rescue a storyteller by providing a "quick fix," such as a joke to lighten the mood. Listeners allow others to experience feelings and live in them as long as necessary to own them as part of their stories of healing.

Call for "I" messages.
Active listeners encourage storytellers to "stay inside their own skin" by using personal pronouns (*I, me, my*) instead of impersonal pronouns (*you, they, one*).

Walk through stories with the storyteller.
Those who open themselves up to caring people around them need listeners to accept their stories without denial, shame, or blame. This will empower

LISTENING

The beginning point of Lafiya is listening.

Listen to stories, poetry, songs, and art;

Listen to words, tones, and body language;

Listen to spoken and unspoken language;

Listen to self, others, and God;

Listen to meanings and feelings;

Listen to generative themes.

Listening is the ability to assess whole-person needs.

Listening is hearing without passing judgment.

Listening is tuning in to the whole person.

Listening is hearing with understanding.

Listening is the beginning of all caring relationships.

A CONGREGATIONAL HANDBOOK

them to move beyond the hurt and toward healing.

Empower others to make decisions.
Instead of saying "This is what you should do" or "This is what I would do," active listeners ask questions such as: "What would you like to be different?" "What are you willing to do to make it happen?" and "What support will you need to do things differently?"

Know how to make referrals.
Lastly, active listeners know when and how to refer people to outside resources without abandoning or intimidating them.

The next few pages provide meditations that help convey what the Lafiya principle of listening is all about.

LISTENING

If I can listen to
* what you can tell me,*
If I can understand
* how it seems to you,*
If I can see
* its personal meaning for you,*
If I can sense
* the emotional flavor that it has for you;*
That is listening
* to you with understanding.*

Carl Rogers

The Art of Listening

Has the following ever happened to you? Halfway through a conversation with another person a bell rings in your mind reminding you of something you promised to do, but forgot?

Maybe it's a word, the general drift of the conversation, or the mention of someone's name. This happens to us more frequently than we would like.

Someone noted that the average adult listens with only 25 percent efficiency. The reasons we hear so little of what is said include:

- *Anticipating the end of the other person's sentence before he or she gets there.*
- *Being intolerant of the other person's point of view.*
- *Being lazy or preoccupied.*

Active listening is hard work, requiring effort and involvement from the listener. One observer wrote these probing lines:

> *As I write these lines I recall the many occasions I've listened, but did not really hear, the reading of scripture lessons. If I hear only 25 percent of them, that means I may have missed some good news that can help me live with more love and hope and faith. Jesus concluded a good number of his parables with "Let anyone with ears listen!" (Matthew 13:43). Good listening calls for undivided attention, whether to the voice of God through scripture or the cries for help from a friend or stranger.*

> *Adapted from a congregational newsletter*

LISTEN

When I ask you to listen to me
  and you start giving advice,
  you have not done what I asked.

When I ask you to listen to me
  and you begin to tell me that I
  shouldn't feel that way,
  you are trampling on my feelings.

When I ask you to listen to me
  and you feel you have to do something
  to solve my problem,
  you have failed me,
  strange as that my seem.

Listen! All I asked was that you listen.
  Not talk or do—just hear me.
  Advice is cheap: 35 cents will get you
  both Dear Abby and Billy Graham in
  the same newspaper.

And I can do for myself; I'm not helpless.
Maybe discouraged and faltering, but
  not helpless.

When you do something for me that I
  can and need to do
for myself, you contribute to my fear
  and weakness.

But when you accept as a simple fact
  that I do feel what I feel,
  no matter how irrational,
  then I can quit trying to convince you
  and can get about the business of
  understanding what's behind this irrational feeling.

And when that's clear, the answers are
  obvious, and I don't need advice.

Irrational feelings make sense when we
  understand what's behind them.

Perhaps that's why prayer works, sometimes, for some people
  because God is mute,
  and God doesn't give advice or try to
  fix things.

God just listens and lets you work it out
  for yourself.

So, please listen and just hear me.
And, if you want to talk, wait a minute
  for your turn;
  and I'll listen to you.

Anonymous

EMPOWERING. Help is not always helpful. In our well-meaning attempts to help others we often create problems that are worse than the ones we are trying to solve. It is human nature to want to give what hurting people need, or to take care of responsibilities for them, or to tell them what to do.

But this creates dependence and perpetuates the status quo. There are times when this kind of help is needed, often urgently, such as when a person is hemorrhaging or starving. But unless the helper can identify and deal with the root cause of the problem, his or her "help" may turn out to be superficial or temporary at best.

A more useful kind of help only begins with listening. The following three guidelines show the close relationship between good listening and active empowering.

• **Listening carefully**—taking a person seriously—helps a person to feel increased self-esteem (empowerment) and ultimately to find solutions that are relevant to the root cause of the problem.

• **Active listening** includes learning how to ask the right questions. This helps people uncover the best solutions themselves. We learn best what we discover on our own, especially in the realm of behavior.

• **Listening that empowers** is a skill that must be learned. It also requires an attitude that all people are worth being taken seriously.

EMPOWERING

A primary goal of Lafiya is to empower persons to take charge of their whole-person health needs and to make life-style choices for health and healing.

Empowering is conveying to others:

> "You are a person worth listening to."

> "You can take charge of your health."

Questions that help empower people include:

> "What in your life would you like to be different?"

> "What are you willing to do to make it different?"

> "What support do you need from us or others? From God?"

Empowering vs. Disempowering

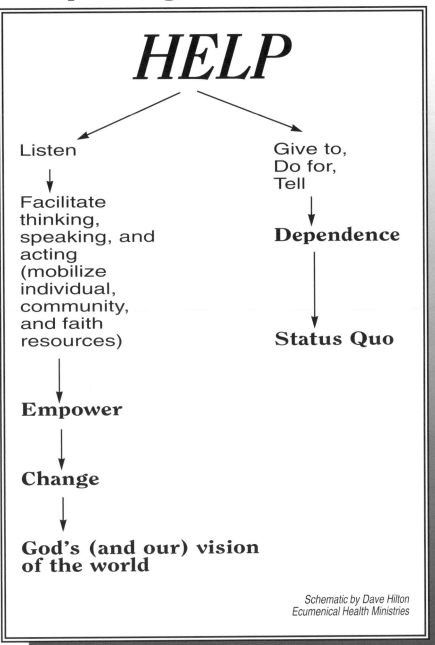

Schematic by Dave Hilton
Ecumenical Health Ministries

The above chart compares the effects of "empowering" with "disempowering," which ends with nothing happening. Listening leads to empowering, and as a result, change. Doing for others what they need to do for themselves leads to dependency and low self-esteem.

When it comes to listening that empowers, Jesus is our model. He took seriously the woman whose presence at the well in the heat of the day indicated that she was rejected by her community. Instead of telling her what was wrong or what to do, he first asked her for a drink. Likewise, he didn't point his finger at Zaccheus in the tree and preach; instead, he said, "I am going to lunch with you" (see Luke 19:2-5).

Listening not only empowers people to break free from apathy, powerlessness, and oppression but it can also be the most effective means of evangelism. Instead of immediately building a medical hospital, a missionary doctor in Guatemala listened to the people's own analysis of their problems. After long deliberation they decided they needed a football field. Instead of pointing out the greater importance of healing sick babies, this doctor helped the Guatemalans build a football field.

The doctor knew that when they finished, they would be proud to have accomplished something as a community. As he had hoped, they soon embarked on other projects that, when completed, raised their self-esteem as individuals and as a community. When they began wanting to address the problem of the sick children among them, they were ready to learn what they could do about it themselves; they didn't want to rely only on the suggestions of an outside doctor.

Today, though the doctor has long since departed, these Guatemalans are still keeping their community healthy through their own health program. They are concerned enough about their problems to own them. But it took the gentle nudgings of a doctor to convince them of their capabilities.

History, however, tells us that those who are liberated from oppression (empowered) eventually become oppressors, as in the French, Russian, and American revolutions. Therefore it becomes clear that we need liberation not only from outside forces but also from ourselves. This component of empowerment is essential if real change is to take place. The gospel is the good news that through Christ we become new creatures, freed to love God, ourselves, our neighbors, and our enemies.

John Vanier, founder of L'Arche communities for the mentally handicapped has written:

> *To love is not to give of your riches*
> *but to reveal to others their riches;*
> *their gifts, their value;*
> *and to trust in them and in their capacity to grow.*

> *So it is important to approach people*
> *in their brokenness and littleness gently, so gently,*
> *not forcing yourself on them,*
> *but accepting them as they are, with humility and respect.*

> *Learning to listen is at the heart of empowering and healing.*

RESOURCING. As a congregation begins to apply Lafiya principles, assessing each other's needs—whether emotional, relational, physical, mental or spiritual—will be one of the early priorities (see Part 4). The term "needs" not only covers a broad range of categories, but it also crosses many levels—personal, family, congregational, community, regional, national, even global. Members of a Lafiya congregation will discover each other's needs as they learn to listen and express their fears and concerns. Listening to each other is also an important way to discover resources to meet the needs.

Lafiya provides an answer to the questions: To whom do we go with our needs? Who is willing to meet us, without condition, where we are? Who can direct us to resources that are "out there," already developed and waiting for us to become aware of them and use them?

Consider the wealth of options

Congregations are not usually noted for their health promotion and healing ministries. But consider how many people value and will say they benefit from regular participation in church life. Also, does it not seem reasonable to assume that children attending Sunday school on a regular basis will develop a healthier outlook on life? Perhaps a slogan for Lafiya churches should be "Church attendance is good for your health."

RESOURCING

Resourcing is the vital task of identifying whole-person health resources within family, church, and community.

Resourcing is providing the link between people in need and spiritual, relational, emotional, and physical resources in church and community.

Resourcing means that a caring church will assure that whole-person health resources are available to meet needs.

Resourcing affirms that allocating resources that minister to human need is an essential mission of the church.

Lastly, *resourcing adopts* an "I'll do it!" attitude:

Three beginning questions:
If not us, *who?*
If not now, *when?*
If not this, *what?*

Congregations are an often-overlooked resource, not because people don't want to care, but many have simply not been taught or "allowed" to be that transparent. But the church is the ideal haven of healing—through its members, the worship services offered, and the comfort of longstanding traditions. Sharing the Lord's Supper can also be a healing and restoring resource as God is experienced in the community of believers.

Another dimension of church life that should not be overlooked lies within the personal skills and gifts that members bring. Many who are trained bankers, counselors, teachers, mechanics, hairdressers, and so on, would be happy to offer their services to others if only asked. Lafiya congregations will find ways to match human needs with member resources.

Healing, anointing, caregiving, and worship

Lafiya congregations provide special healing ministries for members as well as a healing emphasis integrated with regular worship. These ministries include the laying on of hands or the anointing service. Offering the service of anointing has been an integral part of introducing Lafiya in pilot congregations.

Congregational caregiving is another rich resource offered in Lafiya congregations. The range of congregational care is impressive. From informal member-to-member caring to organized prayer chains and visitation programs, most congregations are committed to caregiving. Offering pastoral care is a major function of the pastoral or deacon team.

Worship services especially help members find and know God, the source of healing and restoring. All forms of worship found in a church are a primary resource for spiritual empowerment. Being a part of a welcoming and supportive community is a health-building and health-sustaining experience.

Community resources

Outside the church, many secular organizations offer resources that address needs and problems at a practical, definitive level. For example, school clinics may be good sources of referral information for the common problems of school-age children. Many companies now realize the value of prevention and health maintenance and as a result provide information, referrals, and support for wellness activities. Some even have active physical fitness programs, staff, and space dedicated to keeping their employees healthy.

Local public health departments provide a variety of services to citizens in the area they serve, and they are not just for those who can't afford a family doctor. Learning the scope of what is available from the local health department will probably surprise most people. Not only do these departments offer pamphlets or health education on topics as specialized as Hodgkin's disease, but many offer a schedule of knowledgeable speakers and fitness clinics, and free immunizations. Treatment for addictions and other forms of mental health care may also be part of their responsibilities. Some provide environmental inspections as well as normal epidemic investigation procedures.

As the Lafiya groups live, take shape, and begin to listen, needs will arise that require the expertise of specialists. "Specialists" can be individuals, private organizations, or groups at local and national levels that address needs as diverse as grief and bereavement, child abuse and incest; physical disorders such as heart disease, cancer, and alcoholism; or learning and development disorders. Most of these resources will surface through research of a local phone book or inquiry at a local library, hospital, or social services organization.

It will be useful if at least one member a Lafiya congregation takes responsibility for developing a data base or directory of resources. Responding to expressed and discovered needs is a first priority, but the listing can be researched to cover the most common—and probable—problems in any particular area. A local health department can probably provide information as to what health problems occur most frequently. This listing can then be consulted as needs surface and referrals are suggested.

A sample listing appears on the following pages. Each individual church will want to modify such a listing to fit their own needs and resources. Having a list not only means that resources are available when needs arise, but it also reminds a church of the variety of options available.

Below is a list that will help the Lafiya congregation begin to develop a unique, community-specific resource directory:

LIST OF RESOURCE ORGANIZATIONS

1. *The local public health department* (fill in specifics)

Contact person:_____

Name of department: _____

Address:_____

_____

_____

Phone number:_____

- -

2. *Caregiving professionals in your congregation* (list below and include area of expertise)

a. _____

b. _____

c. _____

d. _____

e. _____

f. _____

g. _____

h. _____

i. _____

- -

3. *Federal Clearinghouses*
   The Federal Government operates a number of clearinghouses and information centers, most of which focus on a particular situation or condition such as child abuse or high blood pressure. Their services vary, but most include publications, referrals, or answers to consumer inquiries. To receive a copy of *Healthfinder: Federal Health Information Clearinghouses*, contact:

Office of Disease Prevention and Health Promotion (ODPHP)
National Health Information Center (NHIC)
P.O. Box 1133
Washington, DC 20013-1133
(800) 336-4797; (301) 565-4167

Clearinghouses currently exist for:

AIDS, Alcohol and Drugs

Arthritis and Musculoskeletal and Skin Diseases

Blind and Physically Handicapped

Cancer

Child Abuse and Neglect

Cholesterol

Consumer Information

Diabetes

Digestive Diseases

Environmental Protection Agency

Family Life

Food and Drug Administration

Food and Nutrition

Handicapped Children and Youth with Handicaps

Health Indexes

Health Information Database (includes an on-line, publicly accessible data base)

High Blood Pressure

Highway Traffic Safety

Housing, (HUD)

Project Share (Human Services)

Injury

Kidney and Urologic Diseases

Maternal and Child Health

Mental Health

Minority Health

Occupational Safety and Health

Orphan Drugs and Rare Diseases

Physical Fitness and Sports

Primary Care

Consumer Product Safety

Rehabilitation

Smoking

Sudden Infant Death Syndrome

National Second Surgical Opinion Program

- -

4. *Toll-free numbers for Health Information*

The Office of Disease Prevention and Health Promotion (ODPHP) and National Health Information Center (NHIC) has a publication that lists and describes toll-free numbers of organizations that provide health-related information. They do not diagnose or recommend treatment for any disease. Some numbers offer recorded information; others provide personalized counseling, referrals, and written materials. To obtain the directory, write or call:

National Health Information
Center (NHIC)
P.O. Box 1133
Washington, DC 20013-1133
(800) 336-4797; (301) 565-4167
(9:00 a.m.-5:00 p.m. Eastern
Standard Time, Monday-Friday)

The toll-free numbers in the directory cover questions about:

Acquired Immuno Deficiency
    Syndrome (AIDS)

Alcoholism

Alzheimer's Disease

Cancer

Chemical Products

Child Abuse

Children

Cystic Fibrosis

Diabetes

Down's Syndrome

Drinking Water Safety

Drug Abuse

Eating Disorders

Fitness

General Health

Handicapping Conditions

Headache

Hearing and Speech

Hospice Care

Hospital Care

Human Services

Huntington's Disease

Impotence

Income Tax

Learning Disorders

Liver Diseases

Lung Diseases

Lupus

Medicare/Medicaid

Mental Health

Multiple Sclerosis

Organ Donation

Paralysis and Spinal Cord Injury

Parkinson's Disease

Plastic Surgery

Pregnancy

Rare Disorders

Retinitis Pigmentosa

Reye's Syndrome

Safety

Sickle Cell Disease

Spina Bifida

Sudden Infant Death Syndrome

Surgery

Trauma

Urological Disorders

Venereal Diseases

Vision

Women

Recorded messages also available from the NHIC at (800) 336-4797.

Currently these cover: Lyme Disease, Cancer, AIDS, Medicare and Medicaid, Health Insurance, and other sources of health information.

----

5. *Cancer Information*
American Cancer Society
1599 Clifton Road, NE
Atlanta, GA 30329-4251
(800) 227-2345

(please see next page ⟶)

6. *Heart Disease*
American Heart Association
National Center
7320 Greenville Avenue
Dallas, Texas 75231

----

7. Sexually Transmitted Diseases
Herpes Resource Center Hotline
(415) 328-7710
(12:00- 4:30 p.m. Pacific Standard
Time, Monday-Friday)

STD National Hotline
(800) 227-8922
(5:00 a.m.-11:00 p.m. Pacific
Standard Time, Monday-Friday)

National AIDS Hotline
(800)-342-AIDS
24 hours a day, seven days a week.

----

8. *Alcohol and Drug Abuse*
Alateen, Al-Anon Family Group
Headquarters, Inc.
P.O. Box 862, Midtown Station
New York, NY 10018-0862
(212) 302-7240

Alcoholics Anonymous World
Services
Box 459, Grand Central Station
New York, NY 10017
(212) 686-1100

Cocaine Anonymous
World Service Office
3740 Overland Avenue, Suite G
Los Angeles, CA 90034
For meeting information, call
(800) 347-8998

Mothers Against Drunk Driving
(MADD)
National Headquarters
P.O. Box 541688
Dallas, TX 75354-1688
(214) 744-6233

National Institute on Drug Abuse
11426 Rockville Pike
Rockville, MD 20852
Call (800) 662-HELP for referrals
to treatment centers and
for information.

World Service Office of Narcotics
Anonymous (N.A.), Inc.
P.O. Box 9999
Van Nuys, CA 91409
(818) 780-3951

----

9. *Health Risk Appraisal
Information*
The Healthier People Network, Inc.
1549 Clairmont Rd., Suite 205
Decatur, GA 30033
(404) 872-2100

----

10. *Anointing Packet*
Anointing packets include a
pamphlet, Bible study leaflet, and
48-page booklet to help congregations understand the role of
anointing in the life of the church
($3.95). Also available is the video-
tape "Is Any Among You
Suffering?" which provides testi-
monies on the use of anointing in
private and public settings
($19.95). To order write:
Brethren Press
1451 Dundee Avenue
Elgin, IL 60120-1694

11. *Health Ministry Programs
That Reflect the Lafiya Spirit*

Adventist
For over 100 years Seventh-Day
Adventists have practiced a healthy
life-style realizing that "the body is
the temple of God" and should be
protected. Most notably they avoid
eating meat and taking any narcotics or stimulants. Recent scientific studies show Adventists have
lower rates of cancer, heart disease,
and most other kinds of illness.

Adventist Information Ministries
Andres University
Berrien Springs, MI 49104

Parish Nurses
In 1984, with prompting from
Granger Westberg, Lutheran
General Hospital developed a
Parish Nurse Project. The program
began when Chicago churches
hired nurses to be "health ministers." Soon nurses in different
areas began taking blood pressure
readings after Sunday morning
worship and giving health education to church groups. They also
helped members with health problems find their way into the com-
plicated system of care.
The nurses soon discovered that
one of their major roles was of a
listener-counselor. As a result, the
nurses began developing networking and support groups for single
parents, recovering addicts, wid-
ows and widowers, and many others with special problems. Parish
nurses became true health ministers. This idea, promoted by the
Parish Nurse Resource Center in
Chicago, has spread rapidly. By

1992, over 700 churches of all denominations and in all regions of the country had parish nurses.

Dr. Ann Solari-Twadell
Lutheran General Health
Care Center
1800 Dempster Street
Park Ridge, IL 60068

Congregational Wellness Course

In 1983 the Mennonite Mutual Aid Society (MMA) developed a Congregational Wellness Course consisting of seven two-hour sessions for small groups. Designed to help congregations begin a wellness emphasis, the course includes such topics as wellness, fitness, living with stress, exercise, eating for health, environment, mental health, relationships, coping with life, and spiritual wellness. Looseleaf workbooks are provided for leader and participants and for a separate children's course. Other published resources include a health assessment form, posters, booklets, films and videos, brochures, the periodical newsletter *Well Now!*, and a "Positive Health and Lifestyle Pledge." The emphasis is on an affirmation of abundant life rather than on prohibitions. In 1991 MMA produced a personal wellness workbook titled *Take the Scenic Route.*

Ms. Ann Reber
Mennonite Mutual Aid Society
1110 North Main Street
Goshen, IN 46526

Sacramental Healing

Sacramental healing is the focus of the Prayer and Healing

Ministries Team who produce the well known daily devotional *The Upper Room*. A weekend course is available to help congregations create their own healing services. Modules address the kinds of healing, relationships between prayer and healing, and sacramental aids to healing and wholeness. The weekend concludes with a service of communion and anointing for healing during morning worship.

Director of Healing Ministries
The Upper Room
1908 Grand Avenue
Nashville, TN 37202-0189

Health for All

In 1987 the Health and Welfare Ministries Program Department of the United Methodist Church produced a program manual *Health for All*. The manual helps local church groups study health from a personal, community, and global perspective and discover their role in making health for all a possibility.

Ms. Cathie Lyons, Associate
General Secretary
Health & Welfare Ministries
Program Department
Room 350
475 Riverside Drive
New York, NY 10115

Community of Care and Healing

The Presbyterian Church (USA) Health Network offers a package called the "Whole Health Catalog." This package contains the book *The Congregation: A Community of Care and Healing* and information about resources on health

issues such as personal health, addictions, mental illness, and Christian responsibility for universal access to health care.

Office of Health Ministries
Social Justice and Peacemaking
Ministry Unit
Presbyterian Church (USA)
100 Witherspoon Street
Louisville, KY 40202-1396

Stephens Ministries

Stephens Ministries is a transdenominational, international caring ministry organization founded by Kenneth C. Haugk.

Stephens Ministries
1325 Boland
St. Louis, MO 63117

The Lafiya Program

The Church of the Brethren Association of Brethren Caregivers (ABC) offers the Lafiya program to assist congregations in developing a whole-person health ministry. In addition to this handbook, ABC has developed an interpretive brochure and series of videotapes. These materials may be ordered by writing to:

ABC
1451 Dundee Avenue
Elgin, IL 60120

----

12. *Other healing resources: (fill in your own list as you compile one)*

PART 3

Lafiya Strategy

Assessing Whole-Person Needs and Whole-Person Ministries

LAFIYA STRATEGY

Assessing Whole-Person Needs and Whole-Person Ministries

Lafiya's ministry of whole-person healing begins with an understanding of real human needs, spoken or unspoken. The basic strategy within a congregation is tuning into human needs and developing ministries to meet those needs. Those who become sensitive to the needs of others will find ways to develop needs-driven ministries. This section will explore the assessment of both needs and the congregational ministries intended to meet those needs. In other words, how well are a congregation's ministries meeting the needs of its members?

Discerning health needs is an ongoing task of Lafiya congregations. When thinking about needs assessment, it is useful to break whole-person needs into specific categories: emotional, relational, physical, mental, and spiritual. It's also useful to consider the different groups of people a needs assessment can address: individuals, families, entire congregations, communities, national concerns, and even global concerns. Those launching a Lafiya program must ask themselves, "Whose needs are we talking about?"

Any group in the congregation can get involved with needs assessment, such as a Sunday school teacher visiting class members and listening to their stories about real experiences, or a pastor and team of deacons who ask members as they visit them whether the church is meeting their needs. These are natural settings for congregational leaders to tune into the personal or family needs of members.

The assessment of needs can also begin with congregational or personal inventories, such as those shown on the next few pages. Surveys are a good beginning point since they help formalize the needs assessment, but many human needs are not so obvious and will not come to light through pencil and paper. That is why Lafiya care groups (see Part 5) are likely to be the most natural setting for assessing needs in all areas of congregational life. Time spent in small, safe groups will help a congregation begin sharing their most personal, hurtful stories.

Your Church's Name

LAFIYA SURVEY

Shared by a Lafiya congregation

The mission of Lafiya is to embody God's love and move the (name of your church) congregation toward wholeness of body, mind, and spirit. Members will be provided with educational opportunities that encourage health and wholeness. Lafiya also intends to provide a safe and supportive environment for sharing while empowering each member to minister to the needs of others.

The purpose of this survey is to assess the spiritual, emotional, and physical needs of the congregation. By your responses, you will be providing direction for Lafiya in two ways. First, your responses will help provide a general overview of the needs of the congregation. Second, your responses may provide a direction for specific support groups within the congregation.

Please answer all questions openly and honestly. Indicate your response by checking the appropriate spaces: 1 = Frequently, 2 = Occasionally, and 3 = Almost Never. Please check the last column headed "S" if you would be interested in an education/support group on that topic. Your comments will be especially helpful.

1. Physical

	1	2	3	S
I need information about:				
Physical fitness	—	—	—	—
Physical health	—	—	—	—
Recreational activities	—	—	—	—
Diet/nutrition	—	—	—	—
Alcohol/drug abuse	—	—	—	—
Sleeping disorders	—	—	—	—
Eating disorders	—	—	—	—
Medications	—	—	—	—
Other:_____	—	—	—	—

2. Emotional

	1	2	3	S
I need assistance in:				
Getting along with my parents	—	—	—	—
Getting along with my partner	—	—	—	—
Getting along with my children	—	—	—	—
Getting along with my family (relatives)	—	—	—	—
Getting along with my coworkers/friends	—	—	—	—
Getting along with my divorced mate	—	—	—	—
Locating resources in times of crisis	—	—	—	—
I need assistance with:				
Retirement	—	—	—	—
Divorce	—	—	—	—
Death/grief	—	—	—	—

LAFIYA SURVEY, page 2

Emotional, continued	1	2	3	S
Job change	—	—	—	—
Marriage	—	—	—	—
Moving	—	—	—	—
Dating	—	—	—	—
Health changes	—	—	—	—
Depression	—	—	—	—
Loneliness	—	—	—	—
Anxiety	—	—	—	—
Relationships	—	—	—	—
Other_____	—	—	—	—

3. Spiritual

I have experienced:

Doubts about God or some other aspect of faith	—	—	—	—
Uneasiness with my present church relationships	—	—	—	—
Uncertainties about my spiritual life	—	—	—	—
Confusion about my life's goals	—	—	—	—
Lack of inner spiritual contentment	—	—	—	—
Questions about my Christian commitment	—	—	—	—
Other:_____	—	—	—	—

4. Comments:_____

_____

_____

_____

_____

If you have special training or talents in areas addressed on this form, please indicate them below:

_____

_____

Personal information:

Age: _ 19 or under
_ 20 - 29
_ 30 - 39
_ 40 - 49
_ 50 - 59
_ 60 - 69
_ 70 - 79
_ 80 and over

Gender:

_ Male
_ Female

Member of this church for:
_ less than 5 years
_ 6 - 10 years
_ 11 - 15 years
_ 15 years or more

Name (optional): _____

ALTERNATIVE SURVEY QUESTIONS

Write Y (yes) or N (no) or D (doesn't apply), for each of the following categories.

Recently have you:
_____ been having difficulty in concentrating on whatever you are doing?
_____ been feeling a loss of desire to eat?
_____ been losing interest in your day-to-day activities?
_____ felt regularly under stress or pressure?
_____ been irritable and bad-tempered?
_____ been feeling down in spirits or depressed?
_____ been feeling nervous or tense (tight in the muscles)?

Are you having problems in any of the following areas:

_____ with your partner? _____ with your children?
_____ with your parents? _____ with other relatives?
_____ on the job? _____ at school?
_____ in your church? _____ making friends?
_____ getting along with others? _____ with the opposite sex?
_____ academic studies or exams? _____ making decisions?
_____ with your cultural background, i.e. race or nationality?

_____ Do you feel you are not getting where you would like with your life?
_____ If yes, to what extent do you feel this is so (on a scale of 1 (a little) to 5 (a lot))?
_____ Do you lack self-confidence?

Do you need help to break a bad habit, such as:

_____ drinking alcohol? _____ smoking?
_____ using other drugs? _____ gambling?
_____ overeating? _____ overworking?
_____ oversleeping? _____ undersleeping?
_____ other? name:

Do you have a problem with:

_____ finding employment? _____ keeping friendships?
_____ existing employment? _____ sleepless nights?
_____ finding housing? _____ adequate income?
_____ periods of depression? _____ a severe financial crisis?
_____ feelings of loneliness?

_____ Are you uncertain in any way of your main goals in life?
_____ Do you feel greatly handicapped through lack of education/training?

_____ Are you having problems adjusting to situations now that you did not
have to face earlier in life (such as sickness, depression, loneliness,
retirement, and so on)?

How much difficulty are you having trying to cope with the above situations:
_____ great difficulty? _____ moderate difficulty?
_____ little difficulty? _____ no difficulty at all?

Have you recently experienced, or are you now facing any of the following:

_____ separation or divorce?
_____ a broken relationship?
_____ loss of your job?
_____ retirement?
_____ unplanned pregnancy?
_____ looking after elderly relative?
_____ chronic psychological illness?

_____ death of a friend or relative?
_____ trouble with the law?
_____ being victimized by crime?
_____ getting married?
_____ planned pregnancy?
_____ chronic physical illness?
_____ other serious illness?

Are you experiencing:

_____ guilt about some act, attitude, or thought?
_____ doubts about God or some other aspects of faith?
_____ questions about your Christian commitment?
_____ uneasiness with your present church relationships?
_____ uncertainties about your devotional life?
_____ confusion about your life's goals?
_____ lack of hope in God's help for the future?
_____ problems in living for Christ—e.g. in home, job, or community?
_____ lack of inner spiritual or emotional contentment?
_____ discouragement about living as a Christian?
_____ lack of Christian growth?
_____ lack of meaningful church relationship?
_____ lack of regular church going?

_____ Do you feel that God has given up on you?
_____ Do you feel that you have given up on God?

_____ Have you experienced any recent changes (for better or worse) in your religious practices, experiences, or life-style? Please specify:

_____ Is there some weakness that you are having difficulty giving up (e.g. bad temper, resentment, jealousy, and so on)? If so, please specify:

_____ Do you feel that you are neglecting your emotional, relational, and spiritual life due to distractions such as work, materialism, recreation, relationship problems, or illness? If so, please specify:

_____ Do you feel uncertain that you are following the will of God in:
career or vocation?_____   choice of partner?_____   other:_____

Are you dissatisfied with any of your life-style choices:

_____ lack of regular exercise
_____ stress-filled schedule
_____ too much leisure time
_____ negative outlook on life

_____ lack of nutritional diet
_____ negative relationships
_____ meaningless work
_____ other:

Are there areas in your own personal development that you wish to change:

_____ poor self-image
_____ lack of self-confidence
_____ lack of education
_____ excessive worrier

_____ negative outlook
_____ lack of communication skills
_____ consumed with self-doubts
_____ chronic complainer

But how well are ministries meeting our needs?

The previous pages provide tools for ongoing whole-person needs assessment. The next step is to examine how well congregational ministries are meeting those needs. Is there a strong connection between needs and ministries? Unfortunately, in many congregations, there is little connection. Church goes on as usual while real needs go unattended. The purpose of Lafiya is to bridge the two: personal needs with needs-driven ministries.

Lafiya leadership will evaluate all church program offerings from a whole-person perspective. What needs are being addressed through congregational worship? Sunday school? Support groups? Resource sharing? And so on.

The chart on the facing page shows six primary ministry contexts that should be evaluated in light of how well they are meeting members' needs. Whatever the area of focus, three questions need to be asked:

1. What is working?
Begin with the positive. The church by definition is a place of health and healing. In what ways is this already evident?

2. What is missing?
Having already identified what is working to bring health and healing, make a list of what could be done, were the resources and commitment within the congregation available. Let suggestions flow freely so that the ideal vision for healing within the congregation is broad and deep.

3. What will we add or do differently?
Only after group members have shared their visions with each other should they begin talking about strategies for implementing their visions. The "dream lists" may need to be shortened in light of a realistic assessment of resources and commitment to change on the part of individuals and groups.

The process outlined above will succeed only in a safe environment in which to address these questions. Whether in a group or a one-to-one setting, nonjudgmental listening is essential if people are expected to share their stories about what they need and their dreams about what their community of faith might become. Here especially, leaders have the opportunity to model active listening and open sharing, training others to do the same.

Too often leaders advocate vulnerability for others without modeling it in their own lives. Thus, the important place to begin assessing whole-person health needs is with the pastor, the Lafiya steering committee, and the Lafiya health promoter (see pp. 74-77). Prior to a congregation's "launching weekend," the steering committee should have at least six sessions in which they learn about whole-person health needs by listening to each other's stories.

(continued on page 59)

Assessing Whole-Person Health Needs

1. The context for heath care assessment may be individual, family, congregation, community, nation, or planet.

2. The process of health needs assessment involves creating a safe place for persons to disclose their whole-person health needs, engaging in mutual listening, empowering, resourcing, evaluating, and prioritizing health needs.

3. Categories of health needs assessment include:

	Congregational Worship	Christian Education	Health Promotion/Prevention	Health Resource Mobilization	Support Networks	Health Leadership Training
Assess	Assess existing worship opportunities.	Assess existing opportunities (for example, Sunday school, adult classes, and so on).	Assess existing whole-person health promotion and prevention programs.	Assess existing whole-person health resources available within the church and community.	Assess existing whole-person support networks (care groups, pastoral care, others).	Assess existing whole-person training opportunities: new members, teachers, deacons, others.
Evaluate	What is working? What is missing?	What is working? What is missing?	What is working? What is missing?	What is working? What is missing?	What is working? What is missing?	What is working? What is missing?
Plan	What will we add or do differently?	What will we add or do differently?	What will we add or do differently?	What will we add or do differently?	What will we add or do differently?	What will we add or do differently?

Remember: Whole-person health includes meeting emotional, relational, physical, mental, and spiritual needs.

ONE CONGREGATION'S STORY

At any kind of Lafiya meeting, stories are shared. That is the heart of the Lafiya ministry: the creation a safe place where people can share the hurts and hopes that make them who they are. Following is a story from a congregation that dared to ask: What is working? What is missing? What will we do differently?

It had been a long journey. They were tired travelers. They had no place to go. No one who knew their story. No one who cared. *No room in the inn.*

But there was an innkeeper. The rooms in his inn were all full, but he saw that the woman, Mary, was heavy with child, and he saw the weariness in her husband Joseph's eyes. So the innkeeper found a place of shelter for them in the stable.

No money. No leadership. No commitment. Many stairs, which, for the handicapped, meant there was no room for them in the inn. No room for them in the church. An elevator for the church building was impossible, they said. They talked about it and rejected it again and again.

Then Lafiya came to the church. It opened our eyes to the people around us. We shared each others' stories. No longer were the questions of money or leadership the most important. Now we looked at the twelve-year-old boy in the wheelchair and wondered what it felt like to be carried up and down the stairs to Sunday school and fellowship activities. Now we looked at the woman with multiple sclerosis and asked how much she missed by not being able to go down the stairs to celebrate the Lord's Supper. Now we looked in the eyes of the man with one leg and said, "We cannot listen to your needs without responding."

Soon we had the elevator, along with handicapped-accessible lavatories, a ramp and a covered entryway, and a new area for after-worship fellowship. Just before Christmas, we gathered while the boy, the woman, and the man cut the ribbon across the elevator door and rode to the fellowship hall.

Now they had found room in our church, but more importantly, they had found room in our hearts.

(continued from page 56)

The strong feelings that are generated by this process will be a useful guide for assessing areas of community life in need of change and the likelihood of persons to make the necessary changes. No program will work until there is a strong inner feeling that life must and can be different. This is why spiritual transformation must be at the heart of Lafiya.

Below are themes that expand the concept of whole-person, needs-based ministries.

Meeting the needs of the whole person through worship

Worship is meeting God, growing in love received from God, and learning to give love back to God. Worship is a whole-person experience that can occur privately, as family devotion, as a congregational service, or in an ecumenical gathering of Christians. Worship is health-giving by its very nature, though its potential for health and healing diminishes when the practice becomes rote and rigid, it fails to address spiritual needs, or when it becomes exclusive rather than inclusive.

Meeting spiritual needs is the primary health-giving potential in worship. Everybody has spiritual needs. Spiritual needs are needs of the human spirit that must be met for a person to be whole, such as the need for meaning and purpose, for relationships, for forgiveness, for hope, for reassurance, for self-esteem, and for peace. Spiritual needs can be met through the relationships we form and the life goals we set, but they can be met ultimately only in relation to God through worship. Thus worship is absolutely essential for attaining and maintaining spiritual health.

How can church leaders know if worship practices are adequately meeting the spiritual needs of the congregation? One way is to distribute a list of spiritual needs such as forgiveness or peace on sheets of paper with plenty of space between each item for writing. Each person can then comment on each need in relation to others and in relation to God, asking themselves What is working? What is missing? What will I add or do differently? Some members may be even willing to share their reflections at a special church service or care group meeting.

Worship as community

The above exercise is for assessing an individual's personal spiritual needs, but the same process works for assessing the spiritual needs of the congregation as they are met, or not met, through public worship. For example, how effectively is the need for forgiveness being met in worship services? Answers may reveal that the worship leader is effectively communicating God's forgiveness but the congregation would prefer more personal and direct assurances of forgiveness such as the laying on of hands.

Any assessment of spiritual needs within a church will most certainly reveal that members strongly desire relationships and bonding within a spiritual context. Nowhere is our relationship to others more closely tied to our relationship with God than in worship. How hospitable are we as a community? How welcome do strangers feel in our midst?

A healthy community is not only open to strangers but reaches out to draw them in, especially those who are suffering and in need of healing. How inclusive are our communities in relation to gender, race, and life-style?

Whole-person health promotion and prevention

What are the existing health promotion and prevention programs within the congregation? Every congregation has an educational program, so that's a good place to begin. The educational committee might review the curriculum of the Sunday school and the adult forum for the past year, as well as any special programs or workshops sponsored by the congregation. Does the current program include biblical applications relating to health promotion and prevention? What is missing? A concern for the environment? A concern for justice in health care delivery? What could be added?

Care groups are vital for health promotion and prevention within the congregation and the surrounding community it serves. Other than the formation of Lafiya care groups, how effective are existing care groups in health promotion and prevention?

Youth groups, men's and women's groups, and any self-help groups sponsored by the congregation can assess health needs within their own sub-communities. In addition, people within the church can look at the needs outside the church body: How willing has the congregation been to share its facilities with community self-help groups such as Alcoholics Anonymous? What can a church do to target needs for health promotion and prevention within the surrounding community? What can a church do at the national and global level to promote health and prevent disease?

Discovering what health resources are already available

In the early planning stages, a Lafiya congregation should survey what is being done in health promotion and prevention by other congregations and agencies within the community. Every effort should be made to avoid duplication. As mentioned before, a survey will be helpful in identifying the unique contributions a congregation can make to the health of its members and people in the community.

Strong evidence of cooperation among churches is already underway. In

1992, the National Council of Churches published the results of a survey entitled *Church Involvement in Health* (send requests for copies to 475 Riverside Drive, New York, NY 10115). The publication reveals how churches in 16 Protestant denominations perceive the health needs in their congregations and communities and how they are mobilizing their resources to meet those needs. The survey sample of over 132,000 congregations demonstrates that the church as a whole is interested in whole-person health. This resource will be an incentive for those churches interested in mobilizing their resources with others who share similar health and healing goals.

It will be helpful to distinguish between the resources needed to meet the health needs of congregational members and those needed by the the greater community. They are likely to coincide since every congregation is a sample of the community, but the vast majority of congregations perceive the health needs of the community to be greater than those of the congregation.

It is also important to remember that congregational members are both users and dispensers of health resources. Providing health care to others even at a cost to ourselves is an expression of whole-person health that will need to be taken into consideration when allocating resources. As churches become more aware of their own needs, they must resist the temptation to focus only on meeting those needs. If Jesus is our model of whole-person health, then the cross is a symbol for the sacrifice we may need to make in order that others might be whole.

Whole-person support networks

The most powerful resource for health in any congregation is care. It is not an oversimplification to say that a caring congregation is a healthy congregation. An examination of its support network is the most important area of health needs assessment within a congregation.

Everybody needs support, though the ideal of rugged individualism in Western culture contributes to the denial of that need, especially among men. Christians come to church dressed in their Sunday best, with their hunger for healing and support carefully hidden from others. This is why all members need to be affiliated with a Lafiya care group and urged to attend regularly (see Part 5 on forming care groups).

Churches that have begun a Lafiya whole-person health ministry say that the care group structure has become the primary support network within their congregation. Listening, empowering, and resourcing are powerful tools for supporting others in their quest for health and healing.

Those who are sick, disabled, emotionally disturbed, unemployed, drug dependent, bereaved, chronically ill, dying, homeless, and abused especially need the support and accountability the care group structure can provide. What are churches doing at the present time to provide this support for people in need? Are churches open to developing care groups as the needs arise,

such as a group for those who are grieving a recent loss?

Pastoral care is the support that most people turn to in times of crisis, such as a death in the family or a fatal illness. A pastor can provide support through an embrace and word of encouragement as people leave church on Sunday morning. But a Lafiya care group might ask during a needs assessment: What is missing? What could be added or changed concerning the care structure of our church?

In most cases, a congregation's need for caring will exceed what any pastor or even team of pastors can provide. But spiritual care is a particular kind of pastoral care, and Christians have a built-in need for the support and direction of others, especially gifted leaders. As people within a care group begin to share their stories, some form of mutual spiritual care will inevitably happen. It may also become obvious that some people are developing a special gift for spiritual direction. When this happens, the pastoral care that congregations need is multiplied on a layperson level.

Whole-person leadership training

Leadership in health ministry is related to role and opportunity. For example, parents are leaders at home but not at school. Sunday school teachers are leaders in the classes they teach but probably not in the adult Bible class. This makes the assessment of leadership training rather difficult. Who should be trained for what and by whom?

If we start with the assumption that every adult should be trained to be a leader in health ministry, what should the leaders be trained to do? The answer is the same, no matter what area of health ministry is being assessed. Leaders need to be skilled in listening, empowering, and resourcing so that they can facilitate listening, empowering, and resourcing in others. This is true for parents, pastors, teachers, deacons, and fellow Christians caring for each other. Whenever this happens in relationships between people and in groups, whole-person health needs are being met.

Below are three questions often asked about needs assessment:

What are some of the opportunities for training people to listen, to empower, and to mobilize health resources for themselves and others?
For most congregations Lafiya care groups will provide the best opportunity for introducing these principles to adult members. Groups that are defined by age (youth, elderly) or need (bereaved, chronically ill) offer other opportunities. Orienting new members to the congregation is an excellent training opportunity. Because of their natural leadership roles, teachers, deacons, and pastors are prime candidates for training.

Should there be formal training sessions for developing skills in listening, empowering, and resourcing?
In most cases, yes, though each congregation, as well as various groups

within each congregation, will determine how this should be done. Normally small group leaders will be trained prior to the formation of Lafiya care groups (see care group facilitator training notebook, p. 103), but the goal of the leaders will be to facilitate mutual listening, empowering, and resourcing within the group, making the leadership role less and less necessary for the functioning of the group.

How would one describe the leadership structure of Lafiya?

The concept of leadership in Lafiya is egalitarian rather than hierarchical. Leadership functions are determined by the situation, not by a predefined role. The pastor is rightly seen as the leader of the congregation, but he or she needs to be listened to and empowered like anyone else. Thus leadership training is training in skills that can be used in relationships and groups both in and outside the congregational setting.

Special considerations for needs assessment

Lastly, the following structural elements need to be kept in mind as Lafiya congregations consider mobilizing resources with others interested in whole-person health:

• First, is there a congregational contact person for information about health resources? In most congregations the task is likely to fall on the pastor by default, but perhaps a lay person or team of laypeople should assume this responsibility.

• The second issue is advocacy for those who have the greatest need for health resources but the most limited accessibility, an issue that needs to be examined at the congregational, community, national, and global levels.

• The third issue is cooperation among churches in mobilizing health resources. Wherever possible, planning ought to be done ecumenically, leading perhaps to an interfaith resource committee or center.

• Finally, be sure to include people with overt needs in the program planning that follows any form of congregational needs assessment. Those with needs must be involved in the shaping of programs designed to meet those needs. An important Lafiya principle is to empower people to take action and make decisions for themselves. Doing for people what they can and should do for themselves is disempowering—the exact opposite of what Lafiya is meant to do.

Needs assessment can become one of the most exciting perspectives a church can adopt. A church that is attuned to meeting the needs of its members will continually experience the grace of God as people learn to help heal each other.

PART 4

Lafiya Structure

*Planning and Organizing for
Lafiya Ministries*

LAFIYA STRUCTURE

Planning and Organizing for Lafiya Ministries

We began with the vision. Then came the strategies. Now we direct our attention to the congregational organization needed to implement the strategies and change the vision into reality.

Some basic Lafiya congregational components will include the following:

Mission statement

Each congregation will need to write a succinct mission, or vision, statement, outlining the purpose of their Lafiya program and the goals they hope to accomplish (see p. 70).

Congregational endorsement

A prerequisite for becoming a Lafiya congregation is the enthusiastic endorsement of Lafiya concepts by the pastoral team and church board. (See application and covenant forms pp. 72-73).

Development of Lafiya leadership

It will be helpful for new Lafiya congregations to spend some time writing "job descriptions" for the following positions. Responsibilities will vary from congregation to congregation, but the general breakdown of tasks provides a useful and productive structure:

Pastor

Each Lafiya congregation needs a point person, although a strong point person will obviously see the need to delegate leadership and responsibility (see p. 74).

Steering committee

This group of people will be responsible for initiating the program. They will be appointed by the church board to provide support and supervision for Lafiya health promoters, including the setting of Lafiya goals (see p. 75).

Health promoters

These volunteers will become the backbone of the Lafiya ministry. Two adults (preferably male and female), respected within the congregation as natural leaders and knowledgeable in whole-person health concepts, will be called and trained to direct congregational Lafiya ministries (see p. 76).

Congregational events

Relationship building will occur as church members grow closer to each other through common experiences such as:

The congregational launching weekend

All congregational members will be invited to a launching weekend event that will consist of both training and motivational experiences. Leadership for this launching weekend will be provided by denomination Lafiya staff (see p. 78 and p. 80).

Planning retreats

Pastors and Lafiya health promoters will meet at least annually for networking and planning retreats along with other participating Lafiya congregations and denominational Lafiya staff (see p. 78 and p. 81).

Lafiya retreats

Care groups, groups of care groups, or leaders of care groups can make plans to tailor a getaway that suits their immediate needs for refreshment and inspiration (see p. 79 and pp. 82-83).

Formation of Lafiya care groups

All people within the congregation will be invited to participate in Lafiya care groups with trained small group facilitators as leaders (see Part 5).

Introducing Lafiya to the congregation

Many congregations have a built-in resistance to a new approach to ministry. Both the concept and name will be "foreign" to most members. In one congregation, some members opposed Lafiya as a "new age" program. Others are skeptical because "the church is not in the health business—that's for health professionals. The purpose of the church is to save souls!" Others may resist because it is another program being recommended by the denominational offices.

All Lafiya congregations began with a few "believers." A core group who affirm the congregation as a health and healing community of faith then become the movers and shakers for Lafiya. They have a vision of the church as a place where wholistic health and healing can occur. They want health and healing for themselves and for others.

This core group then comes up with an effective strategy for introducing Lafiya to their congregation. They may begin with newsletter articles on Lafiya ideas and concepts. The pastor may give a series of sermons to interpret Lafiya and to provide a theological background for the program. Elective Sunday school classes and workshops can also help interpret Lafiya.

One congregation started by administering a survey on health, healing, and wholeness. A group such as the deacons may take on Lafiya as an approach to congregational caregiving. Congregational leaders can then investigate what other resources are available to help explain Lafiya. Inviting people to review this guide is another way of introducing Lafiya to the congregation.

At some point, congregations are encouraged to secure the services of Lafiya field staff to assist in the introduction and implementation of Lafiya. They are trained and available to assist congregations at any level of need.

After Lafiya is endorsed by the congregation, the church is ready to organize for action. Securing both the involvement and support of the pastor is absolutely essential as a first step in Lafiya involvement. Forming a Lafiya steering committee and recruiting two (a male and a female) Lafiya health promoters are the next two critical steps for moving into Lafiya. In some congregations, forming the Lafiya steering committee precedes the recruitment of health promoters. In other instances, the selection of the Lafiya health promoters is done first and they assist in recruiting a steering committee that will support their efforts. Each congregation will need to determine what and when each action is taken.

On the next few pages are sample forms and job descriptions that may help you get started adapting the Lafiya program to your particular congregation.

The Lafiya mission statement

Each congregation needs to formalize its commitment to a Lafiya ministry by constructing a mission statement. Those drafting a Lafiya mission statement should keep in mind that Lafiya is not so much a new program as it is a new attitude and approach to ministry.

Rather than being just one more congregational program, Lafiya's mission is to impact the life of the entire congregation including worship, education, missions, service, the office of deacons, and every other aspect of the church. Ideally, the Lafiya spirit within a congregation will have a definite beginning, but no end. It is meant to become a way of life.

Effective mission statements answer the questions:

(1) **Why?** *(The main reason for Lafiya)*

(2) **What?** *(The services or ministries that Lafiya provides)*

(3) **Whom?** *(The persons or groups that Lafiya will serve)*

(4) **Where?** *(The geographical area that Lafiya will serve)*

A Lafiya mission statement will explain the reason, purpose, and justification for Lafiya. The mission statement on the facing page was adopted by one of the first Lafiya congregations. The statement is a strong—though a bit long—answer to the Why? question. However, it would be even stronger if it also addressed the questions of What? Whom? and Where?

Luke 4:18 is an excellent example of a mission statement in one succinct sentence: "The Spirit of the Lord is upon me, because he has anointed me to bring good news to the poor. He has sent me to proclaim release to the captives and recovery of sight to the blind, to let the oppressed go free."

We would do well to follow the lead of Jesus, whose ministry was guided by this and other clear affirmations of his mission. We are not above our master. Lafiya congregations also need the direction of clear and precise statements of their mission.

Mission statements should never be "written in stone." At least every five years Lafiya leaders should be reviewing their mission and asking for the direction of God in this time in their history. New mission statements are born out of the desire to remain sensitive to human needs and faithful to God's calling.

"The _____[name of congregation]_____ is a dynamic community of faith called to carry out the message of God's love and acceptance of all people. We are, from the time of our baptism, ministers in the body of Christ who are called to be agents of God's love, reconciliation and wholeness.

Through Lafiya, the _____[name of congregation]_____ will answer the call to embody God's love, moving as individuals and as a congregation toward Christ's example of wholeness of body, mind, and spirit. This will be done by putting into practice the following Lafiya concepts:

1. Leading persons to seek God's direction as a first step in creating wholeness in their lives.

2. Encouraging persons to seek health and wholeness by providing educational and support opportunities.

3. Enabling persons to get in touch with their real needs by providing a safe and supportive environment for sharing.

4. Empowering persons to make healthy life-style choices and to minister to the needs of others while continuing their own pilgrimage towards whole-person health and wholeness.

Shared by a Lafiya congregation

Congregational endorsement
These two pages contain forms that you may wish to adapt to fit your congregation's particular mission statement and Lafiya goals. Both are ways to

Application Form for Lafiya Congregations

Congregation _____ Phone _____

Address _____

District_____

Pastor_____ Phone _____

Address _____

The basic concepts of Lafiya have been shared with and are endorsed by the
church board. Yes _____ No_____

The pastor endorses the Lafiya principles of ministry and will be an active
participant. Yes _____ No _____

The congregation has/will recruit two volunteers (male and female) to
serve as Lafiya health promoters. Yes_____ No_____

If yes, include names and addresses:

Our congregation has/will recruit a congregational Lafiya Steering
Committee. Yes _____ No _____

If yes, include names and addresses:

Signed _____

Office _____

Date _____

move beyond a mission statement to a concrete plan of action. The forms are optional and are for congregations who wish to establish ties with other Lafiya congregations through denominational participation.

Covenant of Congregational Participation

We the members of the _____ congregation believe that God calls the church to be a healing community of faith. We affirm our desire to explore more deeply the possibilities of experiencing health, healing, and wholeness in our lives. To this end, we commit ourselves to faithful participation in "Lafiya: A Whole-Person Health Ministry."

1. Lafiya ministry was approved by the congregation through the following action _____

_____

2. The following people have been named to the Lafiya steering committee

_____   _____

_____   _____

3. We have called _____ to serve as congregational Lafiya health promoter(s).

4. We commit ourselves to an ongoing process of assessing personal, family, and congregational whole-person health needs.

5. We commit ourselves to intentional whole-person health education and promotion as a response to identified personal, family, and congregational needs.

6. We commit ourselves to making congregational resources and support ministries available as a means of relating to personal, family, and congregational needs.

7. We will work closely with the denominational Lafiya staff in implementing and monitoring Lafiya ministries.

8. We will participate in "Lafiya: A Whole-Person Health Ministry" for an initial three-year period. We have made our decision to enter "Lafiya: A Whole-Person Health Ministry" and wish to begin the program (name of month and year).

Signed by: _____ (date) _____

(pastor) _____

(moderator) _____

(board chair) _____

The role of the pastor in Lafiya leadership

The pastor is key to a successful Lafiya ministry. It is likely that few congregations will grow in Lafiya vision and understanding beyond the pastor's own understanding and ability to articulate that vision. The worship hour and sermons will always be central to interpreting the Lafiya approach to ministry.

Four key concepts describe the role of the pastoral team with Lafiya. First, the pastoral team is responsible for interpreting the Lafiya vision to the congregation. Second, it is critical for the pastoral team to endorse Lafiya as an integral approach to ministry in the total life of the congregation. Third, the manner in which the pastor models the principles of Lafiya in her or his life sets the standard for the congregation. Fourth, pastoral participation in Lafiya is essential. If the pastor is an observer rather than a full participant, the congregation is not likely to regard Lafiya as very important.

Position: *Pastor*

Position Relationships: Member of Lafiya steering committee.

Position Function: Develop a theological and spiritual climate for the implementation and ongoing support of Lafiya. Join Lafiya health promoters in forming a Lafiya leadership team.

Duties/Responsibilities of Position:

1. Attend Lafiya steering committee meetings.

2. Incorporate Lafiya into the worship service when appropriate.

3. Assist with the assessing of needs in an ongoing basis through regular interaction with church committees and members.

4. Keep Lafiya minister (health promoter) and steering committee informed of identified needs that can be met by means of Lafiya ministry.

Knowledge/Skills/Qualities Desired for Position:

1. Understanding of and belief in the concept of the person as a unity of body, mind, and spirit.

2. Commitment to a whole-person health ministry within the congregation.

3. Ability to teach Lafiya principles to the congregation through normal pastoral channels (Bible study, sermons, one-to-one contact with members).

The steering committee

Every Lafiya congregation should have a steering committee to set Lafiya goals and support the Lafiya health promoters (see next page) both formally (through regular meetings) and informally.

The steering committee will be made up of between five and ten people who have an interest in faith and health issues. The makeup of the committee should include a cross section of the congregation: health workers, professionals and nonprofessionals, and people of different ages, marital status, and ethnic background. Obviously, the pastor and health promoters should be members of the Lafiya steering committee.

Position: *Steering Committee*

Position Relationships: To include the pastor and health promoters and report to the church board.

Function of Position: To support and supervise health promoters and set Lafiya program goals.

Duties/Responsibilities of Position:

1. Supervise and support the Lafiya health promoters.

2. Assist Lafiya staff in educating the congregation on health, healing, and wholeness concerns.

3. Provide counsel to Lafiya staff in assessment and evaluation of whole-person health needs within the congregation.

4. Develop and maintain information center for Lafiya ministries.

5. Keep congregation informed of Lafiya staff activities through announcements, newsletter articles, reports, and so forth.

6. Promote congregational awareness of and participation in Lafiya ministries.

7. Assist in planning and executing whole-person health ministries within the congregation and community.

8. Assist in planning and promotion of Lafiya launching activities.

9. Make sure that Lafiya ministries are carried out within the context of the Lafiya mission statement.

10. Assist Lafiya staff in identifying and utilizing resources to minister to whole-person health needs.

Lafiya health promoters

Using the village health workers in the Nigerian Rural Health Project as a model, it is recommended that two people, male and female, be called to staff congregational ministries. The rationale for calling two is that male and female health issues can often be addressed more sensitively by persons of the same sex. Also, two persons with the right balance of gifts can be mutually supportive in a Lafiya ministry.

In most congregations the health promoters will be volunteers who are appointed by the congregation. However, some congregations will want to make health promoters paid members of the Lafiya staff. This arrangement tends to assure continuity and accountability.

The task of Lafiya health promoters is to assist the pastor in directing the congregational Lafiya ministry. As the title suggests, their primary task is to nurture health within the congregation by promoting healthy life-styles, choices, and relationships. A secondary task is to provide a healing ministry for people dealing with illness, pain, and suffering. Another task of a health promoter is to encourage the use of health resources within the congregation and community.

Recruiting the right people to serve as Lafiya health promoters is the single most important decision a congregation will make to assure the ministry's success. It is important to choose highly respected people who are accepted as natural leaders within the community. They should be vulnerable enough to share their own stories of hurt and healing. They should be good communicators, enthusiastic, and able to motivate others. Though not a requirement, it will be helpful if they have some kind of health or social service training and experience. Last but not least, they should understand the importance of faith in health and healing ministry.

Some congregations may choose to give Lafiya health promoters the title of Lafiya health ministers. Regardless of name, their function is to facilitate the development of whole-person health ministries within the congregation. At times their role will consist of listening to stories, at times assessing needs, at times promoting health, at times teaching and training, at times organizing, at times supporting and counseling, at times allocating resources, and at times simply being present.

Obviously, no two people can do all this as volunteers or even as paid staff. Therefore, it is important to think of Lafiya leadership as consisting of the pastor(s), Lafiya health promoters, and the steering committee. Tasks must be allocated on the basis of gifts, time, and interests.

Each congregation is encouraged to develop its own position description for Lafiya health promoters. The model description on the facing page is adapted from practicing Lafiya congregations for use by new Lafiya congregations.

Position: *Lafiya Health Promoters*

Position Relationships: Serves as liaison to church board, business meeting, and member of steering committee.

Function of Position: Provides oversight, direction, and coordination of Lafiya ministry within the congregation.

Duties/Responsibilities of Position:

1. Coordinate and implement whole-person health needs assessment on ongoing basis.

2. Meet regularly with Lafiya steering committee and pastor(s) to coordinate Lafiya ministries.

3. Promote whole-person health concepts and practices.

4. Identify and allocate whole-person health resources to address stated health needs of people, families, and groups within the congregation.

5. Plan for and organize support systems, including Lafiya care groups.

6. Provide training and support for Lafiya care group facilitators.

Knowledge/Skills/Qualities Desired for Position:

1. An interest in serving Christ and people.

2. Dedication to the concept of Lafiya.

3. Ability to communicate.

4. Ability to model sharing and listening.

5. Some administrative skills.

6. Ability to promote and share enthusiasm.

Congregational planning events

The launching weekend

Sometime after the steering committee has been formed, the health promoters have been recruited, some congregational whole-person health assessment has been done, and goals have been established, it is advisable to set a weekend to formally launch Lafiya.

One congregation found it helpful to prepare introductory materials to share with all Sunday school classes. Then during the three Sundays prior to the weekend launching (outlined on p. 80), there was a special series of church school sessions on health and healing themes. At each session, three or four people were invited to share their own life experiences on such topics as nutrition, exercise, addiction, abuse, illness, emotional/relational injury, and so on. This special emphasis provided a broad-based understanding and support for the weekend launching. Following the weekend were follow-up discussions that defined what the next steps in the ministry would be.

The weekend is planned to inspire and unite the congregation around Lafiya principles of ministry. It is a weekend that provides a variety of experiences and includes the total congregation. On Friday evening and Saturday, the congregation's leaders are invited to participate in training and envisioning experiences. During the church school hour on Sunday, there is an elective class to explore the rationale for congregational involvement in health and healing ministries. Then the worship is designed to inspire the total congregation to accept Lafiya as a biblically based approach to ministry. The worship service can conclude with an anointing dedication service for Lafiya leadership.

Planning retreats

Once Lafiya is launched, leadership must stay motivated and program planning must continue if a congregation is to stay interested. Initially, Lafiya congregations met together for these two purposes. The resulting planning retreats helped congregations learn from each other's experiences and provided an opportunity for ongoing planning. The participants soon learned that these gatherings were essential for renewing energy and gaining new ideas. Now, planning retreats address these four goals: 1) sharing congregational stories and experiences, 2) specific training for some phase of Lafiya ministry, 3) planning for future congregational programming, and 4) inspirational worship and commitment experiences.

Congregations moving into Lafiya ministries are encouraged to work with Lafiya field staff in connecting with other congregations to provide this supportive/resourcing network (see p. 81 for sample schedule).

Renewal events

The Launching Weekend is designed to give the congregation an emotional and spiritual base from which to promote Lafiya ministries. After Lafiya is launched, congregations will need periodic renewal experiences. Lafiya congregations are encouraged to consider some kind of annual renewal event to stimulate new interest and growth.

Planning for some annual renewal experience is essential for keeping the Lafiya spark alive. One model for an ongoing Lafiya renewal retreat is on pp. 82-83. This model assumes the role of an outside resource facilitator. Congregations are encouraged to use outside leadership and at the same time develop their own models of renewal events.

The sample schedules and forms on the next few pages can help your congregation get started in structuring its own planning events.

Suggestive only

LAFIYA: A WHOLE-PERSON HEALTH MINISTRY:

Launching Weekend Schedule

Friday, 7:00 p.m.	Leading/Presiding
Welcome . . . Greetings . . . Singing	*Congregational Leader*
Lafiya Worship	*Host Pastor*
Sharing the Vision of Lafiya	*Lafiya Program Director*
Sharing Wound and Healing Story	Videotape and *Congregational Member*
Closing Reflections	*Program Director*

Saturday, 9:00 a.m. - 4:00 p.m.	
Opening Singing	*Song Leader*
Lafiya Worship	*Host Pastor*
Important Lafiya Ministry Components	*Program Director*
Training for Listening	*Program Director*
Whole-Person Story Listening/Telling	*Small Groups*
Identifying Generative Themes	*Program Director*
Closing Friendship Circle	*Program Director*

Saturday, Dinner Meeting with Lafiya Steering Committee (Optional)

Reflecting on Lafiya in Congregation
Reviewing the Role and Activities of Steering Committee

Sunday, Church School Hour & Worship

Church School Hour	
Rationale for Health & Healing Ministry	*Program Director*
(Adult & Youth Forum/Elective)	
Worship Hour	*Host Pastor*
Planning Order of Worship	*Host Pastor*
A Suggested Text	Mark 2:1-12
Wound and Healing Story	*Congregational Member*
Worship	*Leader/Host Pastor*
Sermon: "Creating a Safe Place	*Program Director*
for Health and Healing"	

Consecration/Anointing Service for Lafiya Workers

LAFIYA WEEKEND PLANNING RETREAT

For Congregations in Lafiya Ministries

	Leading/Presiding
Friday, 7:00 p.m.	
Welcome . . . Greetings . . . Singing	*Lafiya Staff*
Update of Lafiya Happenings	*Lafiya Staff*
Share a Lafiya Story	*Participating Congregations*
(Each congregation is invited to share	
a story from Lafiya experiences.)	
Closing Reflections	*Lafiya Staff*
Personal Time and Recreation	
Saturday, 8:30 a.m.	
Lafiya Singing and Worship	*Lafiya Staff*
Composite of Congregational Experiences	*Small Groups*

- Share with each other what is happening with Lafiya
- Following a period of general sharing, make a list of similarities and differences/contrasts
- Share lists of similarities and contrasts with total group

Saturday, 1:30 - 5:00 p.m.

Personal Time and Recreation
Training Session for Lafiya Workers/Lafiya Staff

Saturday, 6:30 p.m.

Looking Into the Future	*Congregational Groups*
Confess (identify) what is not going well	
Select one thing you wish to accomplish:	
in one month . . . three months . . . six months . . . .one year	
What kind of support/resources will you need to carry out your stated goals?	
From your congregation? Pastor? Health promoters? Steering committee?	
Other Lafiya congregations? The Lafiya office? Any other group?	

Personal Time and Recreation

Sunday, 8:30 a.m.

Coming Together . . . Singing	*Lafiya Staff*
Sharing Congregational Confessions,	*Congregations*
Goals and Support/Resource Needs	
Closing Worship and Commitment Service	*Lafiya Staff*

Do annually

JOURNEY TOWARD WHOLENESS
Lafiya Weekend Retreat

PURPOSE: To provide an opportunity for participants to . . .

- Become more aware of their whole-person health as a life-journey;
- Affirm the aspects of the journey that are health/life-giving;
- Come to terms with aspects of the journey that are illness-producing;
- Experience healing and wholeness through personal journaling; story telling/listening; empowering relationships; and sharing of faith resources.

ATTENDANCE: This retreat is open to all persons involved in congregational life who can attend the entire retreat. Due to the content and formation of small groups, continuity of participation is important. All persons involved in a Lafiya care group, or who anticipate joining such a group, are especially encouraged to participate.

SCHEDULE: 7:00 p.m. Friday-5:00 p.m. Saturday.

LOCATION AND MEALS: To be arranged by local church.

LEADERSHIP: Directed by Lafiya Program Director.

Sponsoring congregation will recruit the following leadership:
- Song Leader (to choose and lead songs on health, healing, and wholeness themes).
- Bible Leader(s) to share three Bible stories on faith journeys.
- Three Persons to share personal journeys; one on mental health, one on physical health, and one on spiritual health.

SCHEDULE	ITEM	PRESENTER
Friday 7:00 p.m.	Coming Together	*Song Leader*
7:15 p.m.	Introduction to Weekend	*Weekend Facilitator*
7:30 p.m.	Reflections of an Extended Trip What preparations were made? By whom? Who went on trip? What was the purpose? Were there surprises/disappointments? What were the high/low points? Was it a direct journey from point A to point B? If not, describe the detours . . . the side trips . . . the flat tires . . . the setbacks, etc. (write in journal - stenographic notebook)	*Weekend Facilitator*
7:45 p.m.	Sharing Reflections of Extended Trip Describe important features/characteristics of a journey	*Small Group*
8:15 p.m.	Presenting a Model of Wholeness	*Weekend Facilitator*
8:30 p.m.	Reflection of Wholeness Model How does model speak to you? Is model understandable and acceptable? What are strengths and weaknesses?	*Small Group*
8:45 p.m.	Closing Worship First Biblical Example of Faith Journey Closing Friendship Circle	*Bible Presenter* *Small Group*

SCHEDULE	ITEM	PRESENTER
Saturday 8:10 a.m.	Coming Together	*Group Singing*
8:20 a.m.	Biblical Example of Faith Journey	*Bible Presenter*
8:30 a.m.	Journey Toward Mental Wholeness Components of Mental Health	*Weekend Facilitator*
8:45 a.m.	One Person's Journey with Mental Health	

9:15 a.m.	Personal Journaling
	    Name your feelings as you listened to story.
	    How is your story similar? Different?
	    What are your detours to mental wholeness?
	    Where have you experienced healing?
	    What still needs healing?
		Weekend Facilitator

9:30 a.m.	Break	
9:45 a.m.	Journey Toward Physical Wholeness Components of Physical Health	*Weekend Facilitator*
10:00 a.m.	One Person's Journey with Physical Health	
10:30 a.m.	Personal Journaling	*Weekend Facilitator*
10:45 a.m.	Reflecting Mental/Physical Wholeness	*Small Group*
12:00 p.m.	Lunch	
1:00 p.m.	Coming Together	*Group Singing*
1:05 p.m.	Third Biblical Example of Faith Journey	*Bible Presenter*
1:15 p.m.	Journey Toward Spiritual Wholeness Components of Spiritual Health	*Weekend Facilitator*
1:30 p.m.	One Person's Journey with Spiritual Health	
2:00 p.m.	Personal Journaling	*Weekend Facilitator*

2:15 p.m.	One-to-One Walk
	Reflecting on our Journey Toward Wholeness . . . *Weekend Facilitator*
	    Focus on walk with disappointments, pain, suffering, fear, guilt, addictions.
	    Where have you experienced healing? What still needs to be healed?	

3:15 p.m.	Final Journaling Reflect on our walk with unresolved hurt and pain, and need for healing.	

3:30 p.m.	Roadblocks on the Journey to Wholeness
	    Share at least one unresolved life issue . . .
	    Some area in your journey in need of healing that you are willing to share.
	    Invite group to lay hands on you and anoint you with oil.
		Weekend Facilitator

5:00 p.m. Closing	Friendship Circle Reflecting on Experiences of Day Closing Song	*Weekend Facilitator*

PART 5

Lafiya Care Groups

*Listening, Empowering, and
Resourcing for Health and Healing*

LAFIYA CARE GROUPS

Listening, Empowering, and Resourcing for Health and Healing

The formation of Lafiya care groups is the only suggested program element in Lafiya. These function not so much as permanent structures in the organization of a church but as seed beds, places for fragile plants to be nourished in a safe environment so they can grow and become strong.

Rationale for care groups

The formation of care groups is the central program of Lafiya because the core principles of listening, empowering, and resourcing can best be realized in such a setting. When these principles become goals for action, congregations become places of health and healing.

It is not enough to inform people about the value of listening, empowering, and resourcing. It is not even enough to explain how to do them. They will happen only if people sense the support structure they provide within a congregation. Listening to each other's wounds in a safe place is essential for healing and the basis for the empowering and resourcing necessary for health promotion.

It is for the above reasons that the formation of care groups is a high priority for congregations beginning a Lafiya ministry. Lafiya steering committees can start by including all members in such groups, even if their participation is minimal, since a caring support group is essential for Christian nurture to happen. Once members taste the benefits of mutual disclosure and encouragement, few will want to stay away from the experience.

Care group structure

Each Lafiya care group will include six to ten people with trained care group leaders as facilitators. Ideally, each group will represent a cross section of the congregation—intergenerational, male, female, single, married, and so forth.

The purpose of care groups

The basic purpose of each Lafiya care group is to extend mutual Christian caring to each care group member and family. Care group leaders will function as facilitators, not as primary caregivers. Caring will be mutual; each person in the group is equal to every other. Each will care for and be cared for by others.

How Does a Group Become

According to M. Scott Peck in The Different Drum, *a group goes through four stages*

Pseudocommunity. At this stage, members of the group try to fake community by being very pleasant and avoiding conflict. Beware of instant communities that ignore differences among their members. People keep their feelings to themselves and pretend they're not offended if someone says something that irritates them. Once individual differences are not only allowed but encouraged, the group almost immediately moves to the second stage of community.

Chaos. Once differences are out in the open, the dynamics of a group usually begin to center on misguided efforts to heal and convert each other. These efforts are misguided because they are still attempts to eliminate differences. Since most faith traditions value healing and conversion, religious groups can easily get stuck at this level. What makes this stage so discouraging to group members is that the struggle goes nowhere and the group seems to degenerate from what, at the beginning, at least had the appearance of community. Although this stage of chaos will cause members to feel as though something is wrong, arguing is actually better than pretending to agree. Often groups will attempt to organize around some task as a means of dealing with their discomfort, but an organization isn't a community. Only as group members begin to listen to each other will it be possible to move beyond this stage.

Small group facilitators

Lafiya group facilitators need to be recruited and trained prior to the formation of Lafiya care groups. The leadership of each Lafiya care group will consist of a team of one or two people. Spouses serving as leaders should be teamed together. Dividing spouses to lead separate groups is generally not a good idea since modern life-styles separate the family unit too much already, and it is best, when possible, to let spouses serve together.

Criteria for small group facilitators

Recruiting the right people to serve as care group leaders is critical. Each steering committee should define the desired qualities and select people with those qualities. Generally, effective small group facilitators are in touch with their own wounds and healing stories and have experienced

...a Community?

of development.

Emptiness. This is the hardest but most crucial stage in the formation of community. Group members empty themselves of all barriers to communication: expectations; putting others into a mold and no longer listening to them; prejudice; unconscious stereotyping based on age, race, gender, or life-style; a closed mind about religion, politics, and values; the need to fix things for others rather than empowering them to find their own solutions; and the need to control the group process rather than trusting the natural emergence of community. What enables defenses to drop and vulnerabilities to dissolve is genuine listening as members of the group share their defeats, doubts, fears, and inadequacies. Though it may seem as though the group is dying, it's really transforming itself into genuine community.

Community. A soft quietness and a sense of peace characterize genuine community. People become gentle, patient, and kind with each other. Feelings of sadness and joy pervade the group at the same time. Though no one is trying to heal or convert anyone anymore, there is an extraordinary amount of healing and converting as people empower each other through listening.

Reprinted with permission.

Christ's grace in their own lives. They are not easily shocked, they can listen without needing to "rescue," they can invite group interaction, and they are comfortable with their own faith without feeling the need to impose it on others.

Oversight of care groups

An oversight team of the pastor(s), health promoters, and steering committee will supervise the formation and direction of Lafiya care groups. Adequate preparation of the congregation through sermons, announcements, newsletters, and so on is important for a successful launching of the groups.

Training small group facilitators

A minimum of six two-hour training sessions will prepare Lafiya care group leaders to help meet the needs of their group. Training sessions will deal with issues such as: creating a climate of trust; listening to wound and healing stories; facilitating group interventions; empowering groups through access of group, congregational, and community resources; knowing when to refer group members to professionals; supporting group members through phone calls and other forms of encouragement; utilizing faith experiences; and so on (see pp. 104-119).

Selection of small groups

Lafiya care group leaders should be active participants in the selection of their small groups. One proven method is to divide the congregation into three categories of members: 1) very active 2) moderately active 3) infrequently active.

Inactive members are not included. Assuming that the three groups are evenly represented, each team leader will select one household from each list. After the first round (draft) they will select a second round, which will give each team leader six households. Six or seven households is a good starting number and provides openings for new families. Conversely, no care group should have more than eight households.

Another option is to include only those who wish or volunteer to participate initially. As interest builds, new groups can be formed, and it will become clear that Lafiya is a way of doing ministry for everybody. A network of support that includes everyone in the church is vital to the Lafiya experience.

Team leader contacts

Following adequate publicity on the formation of Lafiya care groups, team leaders, or members of the oversight team, will initiate contacts with their selected households to invite participation. Personal visits are best, but when that is impossible, phone calls can work just as well. It is advisable to follow

up all initial contacts with notes to confirm the next step agreed upon.

Care group meetings

A series of six two-hour informal meetings launch the Lafiya experience. These allow people to get to know each other and listen to each other's introductory stories. The purpose is to experience the support and caring needed for self and family.

Specialized support groups

As care groups meet to share their personal and family stories, some needs may arise that can best be met in a group with others who have similar needs. While people with acute needs should remain within the general Lafiya care group network, specialized support groups may evolve to address such needs as addictions, depression, grief, marriage conflicts, and so forth.

Inclusion of non-attenders

Some care groups may be made up of people who do not wish to attend the meetings. It will be a challenge for those who do attend to find ways to reach out to the others in a manner that reflects the Lafiya way of doing ministry. Interested members should not pass judgment or put pressure on those who aren't interested; rather prayer or communication chains, phone calls, visits, and notes may show the concern that eventually draws non-attenders into the group. (This is for churches where all members participate in Lafiya.)

Group structure within the church

In addition to care group meetings, a phone and prayer communication chain is an effective means of linking each household within a care group to the larger congregation. Lafiya care groups may likewise be called upon for special congregational purposes such as stewardship solicitations, Lenten/ Advent discussion groups, congregational needs assessments, new member sponsorship, and so on.

Care group content

The content of care group sessions will be the stories that people have to share—stories of relational, emotional, physical, and spiritual hurts and healing. Care group facilitators will lead by example; their sharing becomes an invitation for everyone to participate (the following sections will provide more information about care group content).

At the same time group leaders should make sure that no one is ever pressured to share what is uncomfortable. It will be quite natural in care group meetings for people to draw on experiences of faith and biblical stories to

interpret and integrate their stories of hurt and healing. Focusing on a biblical story of caring is an excellent way to begin each session. Closing each session in a similar manner—with faith affirmations, the healing touch of the "laying on of hands," and group or personal prayers—places the care group experience within the context of the faith that binds people together as children of God.

Lafiya care group meetings

Frequency of meetings. After the initial series of six sessions, each Lafiya care group will determine how they would like to continue. Some will want to meet regularly, perhaps once a week, while others will seldom meet. Accessibility and frequent contact may deepen the Lafiya spirit more than frequent meetings. Some groups will want to meet for extended weekend retreats, but all groups should plan to meet at least quarterly.

Meeting time. Each group will determine the time and length of each meeting. It is important to honor a beginning and ending time for each meeting. If more time is needed than scheduled, the leader should initiate discussion as to when to finish the meeting. It is not advisable to extend the meeting time without group consent.

Lafiya care group meeting format

Opening. Each meeting should have an opening focus statement. Biblical stories, especially Jesus' parables, are excellent for this. Stories that revolve around healing, whether physical, spiritual, or both, help create a climate of safety for people sharing their stories of illness and health (see "Scripture Reflection Possibilities," pp. 94-95).

Whole-person story sharing. Leaders will then invite members to share their whole-person health stories. Initially, each person may wish to use an entire session. Leaders, however, should make sure that each person has had a turn before a second round of sharing begins (see "Suggestions for Care Group Sharing," pp. 96-101).

Closure. Plan for an intentional group closing, such as a friendship circle group prayer for the person or people who shared during the meeting, the laying on of hands, and so on.

Always remember that the role of the care group is to listen, empower people to act, and identify resources for health and healing.

Guidelines for Participation in a Lafiya Care Group

Contributed by a Lafiya Congregation

• I will be present at each meeting of the group except for very serious reasons. I will be prompt, expecting the meeting to begin and end at the agreed-upon times. Remembering that the host has other time commitments, I will not linger after the meeting for a long period of time. (I recognize that sometimes it may be helpful to continue to chat with others, but it can be done at some other place.)

• I will consider that all present are at the same level in terms of person-to-person relationships and contributions to the group experience. In this spirit, I will address each person in the group on a first-name basis, regardless of the custom in other circumstances.

• I will treat every personal statement made in this room as confidential, i.e. I will not tell anyone outside this room anything personal that was shared here by anyone.

• I will listen attentively, carefully, and empathetically to every person. I want to encourage trust so that others may share with me their innermost secrets safely.

• I will try to be sensitive to every person's feelings as I listen and as I speak, conveying as best I can a deeply caring attitude.

• I will be courteous, kind, accepting, nonjudgmental, and helpful in my responses, both verbal and nonverbal, to others' comments.

• I will share my thoughts and emotions when I need to, and I will be open, honest, frank, and trusting when I do. This means that I may express a viewpoint that is different from someone else's, but I will do so in the same spirit as mentioned above—honest, frank, and trusting.

• I will take personal responsibility to make sure that each person in the group has opportunity and encouragement to share as he or she wishes; I will take my turn appropriately, trying not to use any more than my fair share of time unless the group gives me permission.

• All in all, I will do my part in trying to make the group a safe place for all, incorporating a sense of community that includes every person present. I will do whatever I can to make the group a source of enlightenment, strength, encouragement, and guidance. I want the group to help strengthen and heal each individual and assist him or her in the living out of daily life.

Scripture Reflection Possibilities

These scripture reflections can be used in care group settings as focusing possibilities. They are intended to draw the group together around a brief "snapshot" or image of healing within scripture. The group might wish to start their time together by simply reading one of these passages before moving into the time of story telling. Or they may wish to use some of the possible focus questions to center their discussion. Some groups may use a specific passage to meditate upon during the week(s) following their meeting.

Possible questions that encourage discussion about scriptural stories of healing include:

- What is the community's role in the healing of individuals?

- What is the individual's role in receiving their own healing?

- What might scripture say about the nature of God's relationship with creation?

- What might scripture say about the nature of physical, social, and spiritual redemption and salvation?

- How is healing portrayed in this scripture passage:

    as a theological statement about God?

    as affirmation of creation?

    as expression of the Christian ministry of justice?

    as inclusion of the marginalized?

    as reflection of the wholistic perspective of the Bible?

    as empowerment for full human life?

    in relation to the community's values and mission?

    as mandate for reconciliation?

    as a means of proclaiming the Gospel?

    as a sign of the glory and mystery of God?

    regarding the living of human life, or the mortality of the human condition?

Some passages for discussion appear on the next page.

Matthew 5:1-16 - the Sermon on the Mount: Jesus blesses all those afflicted; Jesus blesses all in acceptance (also Luke 6:17, 20-23, Mark 3:13, John 6:3)

Matthew 8:14-17 - Jesus heals Peter's mother-in-law and fulfills Isaiah's prophecy: "He took our infirmities and bore our diseases." (also Mark 1:29-34, Luke 4:38-41, Matthew 4:23-24)

Matthew 9:18-26 - a woman hemorrhaging for twelve years is healed by touching Jesus' garment, and Jesus heals a twelve-year-old girl (also Mark 5:21-43, Luke 8:40-56)

Matthew 9:32-34 - Jesus exorcises a demon from a man (also Luke 11:14-15, Matthew 12:22-24, Mark 3:22, John 7:20)

Matthew 9:35-38 - Jesus heals crowds of people (also Mark 6:6, 6:34; Matthew 4:23, 14:14, 15:32; Luke 10:2, John 4:35, Numbers 27:17, Zechariah 10:2)

Mark 3:1 -6 - Jesus heals the man with a withered hand (also Matthew 12: 9-14, Luke 6:6-11)

Mark 6:7-13 - the disciples are sent to anoint and heal

Mark 7:24-30 - Jesus heals a child who was possessed by a demon (also Matthew 15:21-28)

Mark 10:46-52 - Jesus heals a blind beggar: "Your faith has made you well." (also Matthew 20:29-34, Luke 18:35-43, Mark 8:22-26)

Luke 5:17-26 - Jesus heals a paralytic (also Matthew 9:1-7, Mark 2:1-12)

John 5:2-9 - story of the pool at Bethesda, where people gathered for healing

1 Corinthians 12:4-11 - varieties of gifts, including healing

2 Corinthians 4:7-12 - treasure in earthen vessels: even though afflicted, in death is life

2 Corinthians 12:7-10 - Paul's attitudinal healing: "Whenever I am weak, then I am strong."

Galatians 4:13-14 - Paul's words on his own disability

Ephesians 4:11-16 - gifts of the community together form wholeness and healing, the "body of Christ."

James 5:13-16 - anointing, etc. "The prayer of faith will save the sick."

SUGGESTIONS FOR CARE GROUP SHARING

This is a list of ways in which facilitators can begin small group sharing and whole-person story telling within their groups. These are creative suggestions and not an exhaustive list. Facilitators may choose to refer to the list, or compile a list of their own. The ideas serve as good "conversation starters" in small groups, but they can be used at any time during a group meeting, or at any time during a group's life to help generate sharing and story telling among members.

A-HA! MOMENTS

This activity helps people focus on those moments in their lives when they received inspiration, clarity, knowledge, wisdom, or meaning. An "a-ha moment" could be described as the time when "the light went on" in someone's head—a flash of inspiration, a bit of life wisdom, and so on.

ACTIVITY: Have people take a few minutes to write down three a-ha moments that they have experienced. These can be from earliest learning to present day; what's important is that each person focuses on moments of meaning for them. After this, the facilitator can initiate sharing by having people meet in pairs, or by asking a few people to share their ideas among the larger group.

TIMELINE

This activity helps people look at their personal history and order it in chronologically. A timeline helps people to remember the steps and stages of their lives, and it can be helpful in story telling.

ACTIVITY: Provide people with paper and pens. Have people take several minutes by themselves to draw a simple chronological timeline of their life. They may want to begin by marking the timeline with five- or ten-year increments and filling in the important events, memories, feelings, and so on associated with the various periods. Encourage people to remember and include at least one event from each of their life periods. Share timelines with others in pairs or the larger group, depending on the time available. One possibility would be to share in-depth with a partner, then return to the larger group, asking more general questions such as:

"Did you enjoy sharing your earliest memories?"
"How was it sharing your timeline with your partner?"
"Were you surprised by any of the memories you generated?"
"Was this a difficult or relatively easy exercise, and why?"

SELF-PORTRAIT

This activity will help people focus on their particular characteristics, limitations, and gifts.

ACTIVITY: Provide large sheets of paper (at least 20" x 20") and colored pens or crayons for group members. Encourage people to spread out and to find a comfortable work space in which to draw. Give them about 20 minutes to complete a drawing of themselves, asking them to include as many particular characteristics as they can. The drawings need not look artistic; they simply need to represent the individual. Encourage people to think of their own particular capabilities and gifts and to represent themselves in their drawing. For example, if someone is a good singer, one might put musical notes coming out of one's mouth, or if another has a good knowledge of geography, one might represent one's head with a globe. Each person will draw a composite of themselves that includes not only physical characteristics, but personal characteristics as well. Facilitators may choose to have people share their drawings in pairs or groups of three, or to simply process the activity in the larger group.

EVENT DESCRIPTION

This activity encourages people to focus on one particular memory or event in their lives, using their five senses to remember and describe it.

ACTIVITY: Have people quiet themselves and find a comfortable spot, then begin to focus on a particular event or happening that they would like to remember. Encourage them to take about five minutes in reflection, drawing on their senses to remember the sights, sounds, smells, feelings, and emotions surrounding the memory. Then have people write down their reflections, describing the event with their senses. Sharing each person's memory event can be done in a number of ways—pairs, groups of three, and so on.

SIMILE GAMES

The purpose of this activity is to help people look at their lives metaphorically. It should be done with creativity and a sense of fun, encouraging people to think of new descriptions for their lives.

ACTIVITY: Provide people with paper and pens, allow them to find a comfortable place for writing, and give them about ten minutes to describe their lives in simile. Have them begin with the phrase "My life is like a . . . " and then draw a comparison. Ask them to come up with only one or two similes and then to write a few words as to why they chose these comparisons. Then have them come together in the larger group to share one of their similes and its explanation.

FAVORITE BIBLE VERSE

This activity is meant to get people talking about their favorite Bible verses. The choices will reveal something about what part of the Bible has meaning in each individual's life.

ACTIVITY: Have each person take a few moments to think of his or her favorite Bible verse or story. The leader may want to have Bibles on hand for reference, though people need not remember the exact placement of their favorite story—only the meaning it has for them. Share the verses or stories in the larger group, letting each person describe what his or her verse or story is, why it was chosen, and why it is meaningful.

BIBLE CHARACTERS

This activity helps people think about themselves in relation to a familiar Bible story.

ACTIVITY: Chose a Bible story that will be familiar to people (such as the story of Noah, the creation story, the story of Zaccheus) and read the story aloud in the group. Then ask people to take a few minutes to ask themselves which character they most identify with. If they were in the story, which character would they be? Why? Why not one of the others? Have people write their ideas on paper, then have everyone come together to share their stories in the larger group.

COLLAGE

This activity helps people think creatively about their lives and histories.

ACTIVITY: Provide people with large sheets of paper (about 20" x 20"), scissors, colored pens, and old magazines. Facilitators may ask participants to focus on a particular aspect of their lives (such as early memories, family traits, college years, and so on) or they may leave the decision of focus up to participants. Encourage them to take about half an hour to work by themselves constructing a collage of their memory/life. The collage need not be artistic; it simply has to represent them in some way. Have people come together in the larger group to share their collages.

IMAGES OF GOD

This activity helps people recognize and share one of their images of God. Facilitators should strive to be inclusive of each person's concept of God.

ACTIVITY: Provide people with large sheets of paper and colored pens. Ask them to take a few minutes to quiet themselves and think about how they view God. Ask them to work alone for about 10-15 minutes, somehow representing their image on paper. Again, the drawings need not be artistic; it's the idea that counts. Sharing can be done in groups of two or three, allowing people time to talk about their images and the meanings they hold. Then have people come together in the larger group and share some of their impressions of the activity (Was it difficult to formulate a picture of God? Easy? Why? And so on.).

EARLIEST MEMORY

This activity prompts people to recognize their earliest memory and then use that memory as a way to begin remembering and story telling.

ACTIVITY: Ask people to quiet themselves and get comfortable. Provide them with paper and pens with which to journal. Next, ask the group to take a few minutes to think back as far as they can, all the way back to their earliest memory. Then ask them to take about 5-10 minutes to record their memory in their journal. Facilitators might ask people to share in groups of two or three, or in larger groups, describing their memory.

"I AM" LIST

This activity will help people generate ideas about what makes them who they are. It helps people focus on all the varying aspects of their personhood.

ACTIVITY: Provide people with paper and pens. Let them find a comfortable working space. Allow 10-15 minutes for people to complete an "I am" list. Each person should begin their list with "I am . . ." and then list their characteristics (for example, "I am a sister," "I am a teenager," "I am friendly," and so on). People should continue listing characteristics as long as they can, each time beginning with "I am . . ." At the end of this exercise each person will have a list of "I am" statements that will include both general and specific characteristics. Share the stories in groups of three, or within the group as a whole.

DESCRIBE A JOURNEY

This is an exercise in which people begin thinking of their life journeys (personal stories) by describing a trip they took.

ACTIVITY: Ask people to get comfortable, and then provide them with paper and pens. Allow 5-7 minutes for people to remember and describe a journey they took (a family trip, travel to a foreign country, study abroad, and so on). Next, ask people to share their stories in groups of two or three for about 10 minutes. Then have people come together in the larger group to talk about the characteristics of taking trips. (Characteristics might include preparation time, taking detours, following maps, being late, and so on.) After listing the characteristics of a trip, discuss how different or alike these characteristics are from those associated with a "life journey."

FAVORITES

This activity will help generate creativity and stimulate sharing.

ACTIVITY: Provide people with paper and pens. Have them respond to a list of "favorites" that you provide, allowing a few moments for them to write their responses on paper. Read your list item by item, providing time in between each for writing (or provide them with a prepared list). Your list of "favorites" might include foods, colors, a season, a type of game, a place, an age, a time, a body part, activities, people, and so on. After people respond to each category, have them come together to share their responses.

ROLE MODELS

This activity will help people recognize the effect others have had upon their lives.

ACTIVITY: Provide people with paper and pens. Ask them to take about 10-15 minutes to think of three role models they have had in their lives. Have them list these names and a reason or two that explains each person's influence. Why and how did they impact the group member's life? The sharing of these stories can be done within the group as a whole, or in groups of two or three.

PERSONAL GARDEN

This activity will help people be creative and have fun as they describe their vision for the world.

ACTIVITY: Provide people with paper and pens. Introduce them to the question: "If the world was your garden, what would you choose to have grow in it?" Encourage people to be creative. Some may start with real produce, but prompt them to think abstractly too—food for everyone, peace between nations, a happy family, and so on. Allow 15-20 minutes for people to finish their lists, then have them share in groups of two or three their "visions." After this, you may choose to have each person share one item off their list in the larger group, writing down each response on a group list that everyone can see. This can be your corporate list of hope and vision for the world.

SYMBOLS

This activity functions as an icebreaker. It helps people start talking about something of meaning in their lives.

ACTIVITY: After people have gathered together, have them choose an object in the room that they think symbolizes them, their culture, or their tradition. If possible, have them retrieve the article and place it in the center of the circle. Then go around the circle allowing each person time to describe why or how this object is symbolic of him or her.

TABLE CONVERSATION

This activity will help people begin to examine the dynamics within their family of origin.

ACTIVITY: Provide people with paper and colored pens. Ask them to remember table time (meal time) in their family. What was mealtime like? How did the table talk progress? Give them a couple of minutes to begin remembering, and then provide them with paper and pens to begin illustrating the lines of communication they see developing. Allow people 10-15 minutes to draw their dinner table with each member around it, illustrating with different colors the typical lines of communication between people. For example, "Whenever dad talks to anyone, I represent this with a green line, or whenever I talk to my sister, I draw a red line between us." The goal of this exercise is not to be artistic; rather it is to begin looking at family dynamics people experienced at mealtime. Sharing can be done in groups of two or three, with people explaining their drawings and any thoughts they have about them.

MOST EXCITING DAY (Follow the example of "Earliest Memory," p. 98.)

MOST EMBARRASSING MOMENT (Follow the example of "Earliest Memory," p. 98.)

MOST DIFFICULT THING YOU'VE HAD TO DO (Follow the example of "Earliest Memory," p. 98.)

MOST BEAUTIFUL PLACE ON EARTH (Follow the example of "Earliest Memory," p. 98.)

TRAINING NOTEBOOK FOR CARE GROUP FACILITATORS

On the next few pages is a "mini-book" for care group facilitators. It is written in a notebook fashion, and it is designed to include facilitators' notes as they learn and grow along with their group. The pages focus on specific skills facilitators will want to develop as they listen to, empower, and provide resources for their group.

THE
FACILITATOR'S
GUIDE

LAFIYA CARE GROUP FACILITATORS

The Basic Task of Care Group Facilitators is to Facilitate...

Care Group Listening
Care Group Empowering
Care Group Resourcing

The next few pages review interaction techniques that help apply the basic principles of Lafiya. Use the extra space on the pages to record your own reactions to or experiences with these principles. Both facilitators and care group participants can benefit from studying how to become better listeners, empowerers, and resourcers.

FACILITATING CARE GROUPS:
Listening...

Invite the group to reflect back to the storyteller what the group is hearing, what they sense the speaker is feeling, and what they perceive to be the meaning of the person's story.

Use open-ended questions to involve the group, such as:
   What is your understanding of what he/she is saying?

Repeat back to him/her what you hear him/her saying.
   What do you sense he/she is feeling as he/she tells his/her story?

Share with him/her what feelings you sense he/she is feeling.
   What is the meaning of his/her story to him/her?

State in your own words what you think the story means to him/her.
   "Is there more to your story that you wish to share with us?" or
   "Is there anything else you wish to share?"

Additional notes on listening:

FACILITATING CARE GROUPS:
Empowering...

When a full story has been heard, invite the storyteller to share with the group what he/she would like different.

> *What would you like to be different?*
> *How would you like your life to be changed?*

Invite the group to reflect back to the person what he/she would like different/improved in his/her life.

When the person describes what should be changed, invite that person to state what he/she might do to make it happen.

> *What steps might you take to make those changes?*
> *What could you do to take charge of your life?*

Invite the group to share additional challenges the storyteller might try in an effort to take charge of his/her life—but be light on "shoulds."

After the storyteller identifies the actions he/she is willing to take, ask him/her what support will be needed.

> *What can our group do to support you in your decision?*

Additional notes on empowering:

FACILITATING CARE GROUPS:
Resourcing...

Invite the storyteller to share what resources are needed to carry out proposed actions.

> *What resources will you need to follow through?*
> *What additional resources will you need?*

Invite the group to brainstorm on the resources available to him/her.

> *What additional resources are available for the storyteller?*
> *What resources does the group have to share with the person?*
> *What resources are available through the church and/or community?*

Invite group to identify community/church resources.

Additional notes on resourcing:

EFFECTIVE SMALL GROUP FACILITATORS ARE:

1. Vulnerable with their own wounds and healing experiences.

2. Aware of Christ's grace in their own lives.

3. Not shocked easily by stories of others.

4. Capable of listening without needing to rescue.

5. Able to involve the group in listening, empowering, and resourcing.

6. Comfortable with their own and others' faith experiences.

7. Aware of their own needs and of appropriate time to share.

8. Understanding of inclusive group process.

9. Sensitive to each person's feelings and participation.

10. Aware of time/group commitments.

On the next few pages are training guidelines to assist those facilitating care groups. Write your own notes or reactions in the spaces provided at the bottom of each page and keep for reference.

EFFECTIVE SMALL GROUP FACILITATORS ARE:

1. *Vulnerable with their own wounds and healing experiences.*

Leaders model vulnerability.

Group members are rarely more vulnerable than their leaders.

Begin by sharing your own wounds and healing.

Your sharing will create a climate for others to share.

One way to begin sharing is to develop a timeline of your whole-person health story.

Birth -- *Present*

> *Identify by date your wounds . . . illnesses . . . accidents . . . hurts . . . crises . . . failures . . . disappointments . . . depression ...*

> Share healing or lack of healing experienced with those events.

Nonjudgmental listening enhances vulnerability.

Create a climate of trust.

Additional comments on creating a climate of vulnerability:

EFFECTIVE SMALL GROUP FACILITATORS ARE:

2. *Aware of Christ's grace in their own lives.*

Are you aware of faith experiences such as forgiveness, repentance, conversion, salvation, reconciliation, and so on in your own life?

Many leaders assume that grace is for others and seldom refer to their own need to experience grace.

Identify the times in your life when the meaning of grace became for you more than a concept—it was a real experience.

Sing "Amazing Grace!"

What phrases in that song speak of your own experience of grace?

Additional reflections on personal experiences of grace:

EFFECTIVE SMALL GROUP FACILITATORS ARE:

3. Not shocked easily by stories of others.

Hurting persons will generally not share fully with persons who become uneasy with their stories.

We communicate "shock" with our tone of voice, body language, eye contact, questions, etc.

Shocked listeners create a climate of mistrust.

Be open about your experience of discomfort.

Circle any of the following issues that would create discomfort in you:

> Adultery - Homosexuality - Obesity - Drug Addiction - Smoking - Abortion - Unmarried Pregnancy - Child Abuse - Spouse Abuse - Mixed Marriages - Pre-Marital Sex - Suicide - Homicide - HIV/AIDS - Divorce - Marital Affair - Bankruptcy - Gun Control - Militarism - Pacifism - Other . . .

> Be upfront about what shocks you.

You show integrity when you name those things that cause you discomfort.

If you are uncomfortable, chances are someone else is also uncomfortable.

Check with the group if they are able to hear the story . . . if not, find another person, or a group of people, to hear the storyteller's story.

Additional guidelines for listening without shock:

EFFECTIVE SMALL GROUP FACILITATORS ARE:

4. *Capable of listening without needing to rescue.*

There is a tendency among caring persons to rescue too quickly, to try to make it all better.

People need listening *through* the pain, not rescuing *from* the pain.

What are your first instincts when a person cries?

If you listen carefully to people, you will empower them to make whatever decision they need to make about their situation.

When is rescuing appropriate?

What behaviors indicate that you are capable of listening without rescuing?

What behaviors indicate when you are trying to rescue?

Role-play: "I was just fired. I don't know what I'm going to do. I can't face my wife or family. I feel like a failure. It wasn't fair." Give a "rescuing" response, then a "listening" response.

Additional suggestions for listening instead of rescuing:

EFFECTIVE SMALL GROUP FACILITATORS ARE:

5. *Able to involve the group in listening, empowering, and resourcing.*

The most important task of small group leaders is to involve the group in listening, empowering, and resourcing.

Effective small group leaders do not keep the focus on themselves. They know how to involve others in a nonthreatening way.

Facilitators know how to invite interaction among group members, such as:

> *Reflect back to [name of person] what you have been hearing.*
> *Share with [name of person] what you sense she is feeling.*
> *What do you want to say to [name of person] to assure him that she is still OK?*
> *Now that you have heard [her] story, what would you like to say to [her]?*
> *What questions would you like to ask?*
> *What resources would you like to recommend that might be of help?*

Facilitate people speaking directly to each other and not to each other through you.

Identify ways to involve group in listening, empowering, resourcing.

Additional reflections on ways to involve the group :

EFFECTIVE SMALL GROUP FACILITATORS ARE:

6. *Comfortable with their own and others' faith experiences.*

Persons with a mature faith tend to be tolerant of others' faith experiences.

Intolerance of others is a sign of insecurity on our part.

The need to change others is often an indication that we are uncomfortable with ourselves.

Ask yourself:

> *What opinions, ideas, philosophies, ideals, religions, and values do I*
> *   have the least tolerance for?*
> *Of what faith ideas am I most intolerant?*
> *Where am I most rigid about my faith?*

Spend a few moments with another person to share some central faith ideas that you hold dear.

> *How comfortable are you in sharing your faith?*
> *How comfortable are you when hearing a faith story?*

Additional considerations on being comfortable with faith:

EFFECTIVE SMALL GROUP FACILITATORS ARE:

7. *Aware of their own needs and of appropriate time to share.*

Effective facilitators are aware of and willing to express their own needs in a group.

They deal with their needs in constructive ways so they can relate to others in helpful ways.

A constructive way of dealing with personal needs is to confess them.

> "Tonight I'm feeling very depressed. I just can't believe what happened to me today. I hope my depression will not interfere in our group sharing tonight. If my depression continues, I will want to share more about this with you at some other time."

Identify in the group when your own needs may disrupt the small group sharing.

Share creative ways of dealing with personal needs.

Additional comments on dealing with our personal needs as facilitators:

EFFECTIVE SMALL GROUP FACILITATORS ARE:

8. *Understanding of inclusive group process.*

The art of including others in sharing and making decisions is a key function of the small group facilitator.

Including others at the level of their interest doesn't just happen. People feel included because groups learn how to be inclusive.

There are three important components to group development:

1. Inclusion
2. Control
3. Affection

Including others in listening, in decision making, in affection giving and receiving are fundamental to nurturing a mature care group.

Effective facilitators do not keep the center of interactions on themselves. They quickly share leadership and include others at all levels of small group life.

Identify behaviors that keep self in center:

Identify behaviors that include others in group process:

Additional comments on inclusive group process:

EFFECTIVE SMALL GROUP FACILITATORS ARE:

9. *Sensitive to each person's feelings and participation.*

Group facilitators will tune in to both storytellers and story listeners. Being sensitive to both is extremely important to bonding as a small group.

People are encouraged to become good listeners through affirmation of good responses.

Pay attention to group members whose behavior suddenly changes. It is a sign that something is going on inside. Invite people to share where they are or what has happened.

Facilitators demonstrate sensitivity when they invite persons, in a gentle tone, to share their feelings either as a listener or speaker.

Never assume you know what a person is feeling or thinking.

Make a list of behaviors that demonstrate sensitivity to group members' feelings and participation.

Additional thoughts on small group sensitivity:

EFFECTIVE SMALL GROUP FACILITATORS ARE:

10. *Aware of time/group commitments.*

One subtle way of building trust is to honor time. There is a time to begin and a time to end.

There are other commitments to the group that require attention, such as attendance, confidentiality, referring to other resources, and so on.

Invite group to make decisions about time and group commitments:

> *Will meeting begin at stated time or when all have arrived?*
> *Will meeting be held if one is absent? Two? Three?*
> *When and how will meetings be cancelled?*
> *How long will sessions last?*
> *How will you manage time?*
> *Will you honor closing times?*
> *How will you deal with unfinished items?*
> *How will you deal with confidentiality?*
> *How will you know when the content of a person's story is beyond the ability of your group to respond helpfully?*

Your answer to these kinds of questions will determine much about the character of your group.

In groups of two, develop guidelines on time/group commitments. Then discuss these in the larger group in order to reach a consensus.

Additional items to consider on time/group commitments:

EVALUATION: SPRING-SUMMER 1993
Lafiya Care Group Experience
Shared by a Lafiya congregation

Filling out this form will help care group facilitators and Lafiya staff evaluate the care group experience in the local church. It can be adapted to ask questions that reflect the needs and concerns of any specific Lafiya context.

Please check either Yes or No. Please explain No answers in the comments area below.

1. My participation in a Lafiya care group was a positive experience. _____Yes _____No

2. My experience met or surpassed my expectations. _____Yes _____No

3. The format/structure of my group was satisfactory. _____Yes _____No

4. The group facilitator(s) were effective. _____Yes _____No

5. I experienced a new level of Christian care and support. _____Yes _____No

Facilitators only: Please answer these additional questions:

1. I found the facilitator training to be adequate. _____Yes _____No

2. The monthly Lafiya facilitator meetings were worthwhile. _____Yes _____No

3. Appropriate and adequate resources were available. _____Yes _____No

Comments/suggestions for future Lafiya care groups (LCGs):_____

_____

_____

_____

_____

- -

Tear off and submit separately by (give date)

1. I would like to continue in my current LCG this fall. _____Yes _____No

2. I would like to continue in a different LCG this fall. _____Yes _____No

3. I would like to continue as a Lafiya facilitator. _____Yes _____No

4. I am not currently a facilitator but am interested in being one. _____Yes _____No

_____
Signed

FURTHER READING
FOR HEALTH AND HEALING MINISTRY

Allen, Paula Gunn. *Grandmothers of the Light: A Medicine Woman's Sourcebook*. Boston: Beacon Press, 1991. A collection of Native American myths that continue to guide females toward an understanding of the sacred.

Antonovsky, Aaron. *Unraveling the Mystery of Health: How People Manage Stress & Stay Well*. San Francisco: Jossey-Bass Publications, 1987. Sociological study that focuses on who stays well rather than on who gets sick.

Bakken, Kenneth. *Call to Wholeness*. New York: Crossroads, 1985. A physician/pastor shares his vision for whole-person health. *The Journey Toward Wholeness* is a sequel (1988) that gives direction on how to do health ministry.

Borysenko, Joan. *Minding the Body, Mending the Mind*. New York: Bantam, 1987. An examination of the intricate relationship between the human components of mind, body, spirit.

Brody, Howard. *Stories of Sickness*. New Haven: Yale University Press, 1987. Shows how important stories are for understanding health, illness, and healing.

Coles, Robert. *The Call of Stories*. Boston: Houghton Mifflin, 1989. A great story-teller shows the power of stories.

Cousins, Norman. *Head First: The Biology of Hope*. New York: E.P. Dutton, 1989. A persuasive case for the importance of hope in healing.

Droege, Thomas. *The Faith Factor in Healing*. Philadelphia: Trinity Press International, 1991. A study of the role that faith plays in medical practice and the church's health and healing ministry.

Droege, Thomas. *The Healing Presence*. San Francisco: Harper Collins, 1992. A manual of guided imagery exercises for health, healing, and recovery. For personal use as a pastoral care resource, and for use in groups.

Erdman, Mardi. *Undercover Exercise*. Englewood Cliffs: Prentice-Hall, 1984. A practical guide to physical exercises and stretches that can be done by someone confined to bed.

Frank, Arthur. *At the Will of the Body*. Boston: Houghton Mifflin, 1991. A riveting personal narrative of a young man who suffered a heart attack and an occurrence of cancer within two years.

Gibble, June and Swartz, Fred, eds. *Called to Caregiving*. Elgin: Brethren Press, 1987. A resource equipping deacons and other lay caregivers.

Haugk, Kenneth C. *Christian Caregiving, A Way of Life*. Minneapolis: Augsburg, 1984. By the director of Stephens Ministries. A leader's guide is also available.

Granberg-Michaelson, Karin. *Healing Community*. Geneva: World Council of Churches, 1991. A clear and readable description of the church as a healing community.

Nouwen, Henri. *The Wounded Healer*. New York: Doubleday, 1979. Well-known contemplative author uses Jesus as a paradigm of a wounded healer.

Healers on Healing. Los Angeles: Jeremy P. Tarcher, Inc., 1989. Thirty-seven essays in which contributors explore the complex nature of healing from many viewpoints.

Keck, L. Robert, *Sacred Eyes*. Boulder: Synergy Associates, Inc., 1993. *Sacred Eyes* is a penetrating vision into humanity's soul as it explores life's big questions. The book shows a meaningful progression of physical, mental, and spiritual evolution, and how the "texts" of stories fit into the "context" of humanity's story.

Ramshaw, Elaine. *Ritual and Pastoral Care*. Philadelphia: Fortress, 1987. An engaging discussion of how worship can be shaped by attending to health and healing principles.

Rossman, Martin. *Healing Yourself*. New York: Pocket Books, 1987. A readable account of how individuals can take charge of their health and healing.

Schmidt, Stephen. *Living with Chronic Illness*. Minneapolis: Augsburg, 1989. The author shares the story of his struggle with chronic illness and tells about the formation of a support group, in which members share stories, for the chronically ill.

Siegel, Bernie. *Love, Medicine, and Miracles* and *Peace, Love, Healing*. San Francisco: Harper, 1986. Lessons learned about self-healing from a surgeon's experience.

Tournier, Paul. *A Listening Ear*. London: Hodder & Stoughton, 1984. This well-known Christian physician has written many popular books on the meaning of whole-person health and healing. This one describes the art of listening.

Westberg, Granger. *The Parish Nurse*. Park Ridge: Parish Nurse Resource Center, 1987. The founder of the parish nurse movement gives simple directions on how to start a congregational parish nurse program.

Wuellner, Flora Slosson. *Prayer, Stress, & Our Inner Wounds*. Nashville: The Upper Room, 1985. A marvelous resource on Christian spirituality and healing, as is *Prayer & Our Bodies*. A good resource for exercises and discussion in small groups.